P9-DXO-433

# WORLDS AROUND THE SUN

# WORLDS AROUND THE SUN

## by Lee Edson

*Consultant*
**CARL SAGAN**

*Director, Laboratory for Planetary Studies and*
*Associate Professor of Astronomy*
*Center for Radiophysics and Space Research*
*Cornell University*

*This special edition is printed and distributed by arrangement*
*with the originators and publishers of The Smithsonian Library,*
AMERICAN HERITAGE PUBLISHING CO., INC.
*in association with* THE SMITHSONIAN INSTITUTION

E. M. HALE AND COMPANY, *Eau Claire, Wisconsin*

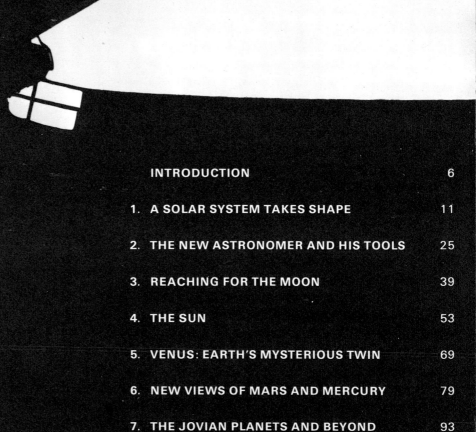

FRONT COVER: *The sun, centerpiece of our solar system, is haloed by its corona during a total eclipse.*
FRONTISPIECE: *The sun ejects huge tongues of gas, some much larger than the earth, outward toward space.*
BELOW: *A man is dwarfed beneath Mount Palomar's 200-inch reflecting telescope, largest in the world.*

# INTRODUCTION

On the wall of an ancient Spanish cave explorers recently found a prehistoric drawing that crudely depicts herds of animals the cavemen hunted. Here and there throughout the picture are what look like suns, drawn in child-like fashion with radiating spokes. They give us evidence that the celestial bodies have always had a special significance for man. Primitive man was no doubt as thankful for the warming, illuminating sun and the regularity of its cycle as he was awed by the spectacle of the moon and stars in the dark of night. When man at last settled down to a life of agriculture, the sun and the moon became the significant regulators of his existence. They served as the basis of his calendar, guides to the length of the seasons, and hence signals of when to sow his seed and when to harvest.

Imaginative men saw patterns in the fixed stars, outlines of objects and creatures familiar to them, and they gave them religious importance. Unusual events in the heavens took on even more mystical significance. The early Chinese, for example, saw eclipses and thought dragons were eating the sun. They believed these strange events to be portents for the future. Two astronomers in early China were put to death for failing to warn the king of an eclipse, the omen for success in battle.

At Stonehenge in England, in the second millennium B.C., an edifice of monumental stone blocks was erected which, according to one modern astronomer, was used as a sort of computer for predicting the motions and eclipses of the sun and moon, events of special religious importance.

At some unrecorded point in time, observers of the skies perceived that some of the "stars" had fixed positions, while others slowly moved in relation to the "fixed" stars. Over a period of months some of these moving stars seemed to slow to a stop, then reverse their courses. The Chaldeans and Babylonians observed that they kept to a narrow belt, known as the zodiac, and later the Greeks called them *planētēs*, meaning wanderers.

For early astronomers, the earth, of course, was the center of all things, and the heavens moved around it. It took the Greeks to develop some of the modern ideas of the sun and planets; Thales, in the seventh century B.C., envisioned the earth as circular, but thought of it as a disk floating in a watery universe. Heraclides suggested that the earth rotates on its axis, and Aristarchus of Samos that it orbits the sun. Yet these ideas had little permanent effect. For sixteen centuries most men continued to believe that the sky moved around the earth (as anyone could plainly see) and that the earth was the fixed center of the universe.

In the sixteenth and seventeenth centuries, the period of astronomy's renaissance, the earth took its rightful place as a planet, moving like the other planets, and the sun assumed the pivotal spot in the center of the solar system. As the telescope, the new instrument of investigation, increased in size and versatility and revealed things never before known, the universe loomed bigger and bigger, and man correspondingly seemed smaller and smaller.

The great reaches of space became the focus of attention. The growing application of physics to the stars drew students to stellar astronomy. The planetary sciences, which had remained strong until the turn of the last century, continued to lose support during the 1920's and 1930's. Even within the past decade, the U.S. space agency has been financing the building of optical telescopes in part to encourage student interest in the solar system.

Today there is a dramatic change in the making, a refocusing on the celestial bodies closer to home. New instruments have increased our knowledge of the solar system enormously. Some of the planets—and, of course, the moon —have been probed by space vehicles flying by or actually landing, and our technology has advanced to a stage where we are able to conduct direct experiments on celestial bodies.

Moreover, we have acquired new ways of looking at the solar system by studying radiation at wavelengths other than the visible light. By making observations from above the earth's atmosphere, it has been possible to eliminate atmospheric absorption and distortion and to learn new things about the celestial bodies that only this radiation can reveal.

A new kind of astronomer has appeared on the horizon—one to whom interplanetary travel and extraterrestrial experiments are as natural as the telescope. His work promises results in knowledge of far-reaching importance to man. "We live on the threshold of a new era, whose effects will reach into the fabric of our civilization," says Fred Whipple, director of the Smithsonian Astrophysical Observatory. "What we do with this knowledge will determine our future for centuries to come."

*The great stone circle at Stonehenge, on England's Salisbury Plain, has long been a source of wonder and mystery. Recently, Gerald Hawkins, an astronomer at the Smithsonian Astrophysical Observatory, has suggested that this relic of an ancient British culture may have served as an intricate astronomical computer. Using a modern electronic computer, Hawkins figured out the significance of the placement of each stone. As the diagram shows, the sighting stone to the northeast of the main circle of sarsen stones marks the exact spot over which midsummer sunrise can be viewed from the monument's center. Through five trilithons, or archways, inside the circle, a viewer could sight summer and winter solstice positions of the rising and setting sun and moon. The outer ring of 56 stones may have been an eclipse computer.*
OVERLEAF: *Viewed through the sarsen circle, a midsummer sun rises above the ancient sighting stone.*

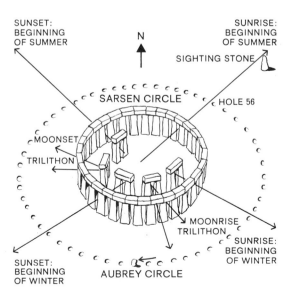

SUNSET: BEGINNING OF SUMMER

SUNRISE: BEGINNING OF SUMMER

N

SIGHTING STONE

SARSEN CIRCLE

HOLE 56

MOONSET

TRILITHON

MOONRISE TRILITHON

SUNRISE: BEGINNING OF WINTER

SUNSET: BEGINNING OF WINTER

AUBREY CIRCLE

# 1. A SOLAR SYSTEM TAKES SHAPE

Almost any schoolboy can, especially if pressed a bit, conjure up a mental picture of the solar system, that merry-go-round of nine relatively tiny objects circling a huge, hot, central sun. The planets move in orbits almost all in one plane but at different speeds: the innermost, Mercury, circumnavigates the sun in 88 days; the farthest, Pluto, takes 248 years to make the same trip. The schoolboy is also likely to know that distances in the solar system are very great. Mercury is thirty-six million miles from the sun, while Pluto is almost four billion miles away. Venus, our nearest planetary neighbor, never comes closer to earth than twenty-five million miles.

Nowadays, awareness of the sun and its far-flung family is commonplace. Yet it took man an incredibly long time to agree that planets were indeed worlds, to list our earth as one of them, to believe they were revolving in fixed orbits around the sun—in short, to discover the solar system.

The basic problem is that of imagining a model that will explain the motion of the sun and planets in relatively simple terms. It must make sense to an observer standing outside the solar system; if he stands on earth it must also agree with what he actually sees.

The five astronomers chiefly responsible for postulating, expanding, and refining the model of the solar system that we accept today were men of different backgrounds and personalities: Copernicus was a Pole, Tycho Brahe a Dane, Kepler a German; Galileo was Italian and Newton was English. Their life spans bridged two and a half centuries, from 1473, the year

*A starstruck medieval scholar marvels at the planets' movements in concentric spheres.*

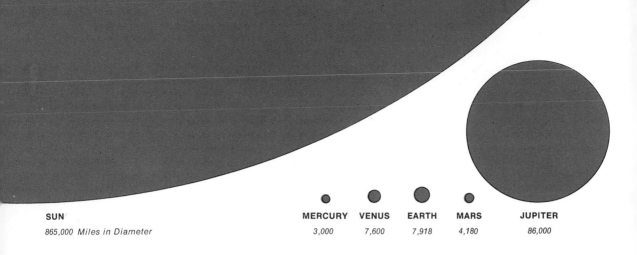

SUN
*865,000 Miles in Diameter*

MERCURY 3,000

VENUS 7,600

EARTH 7,918

MARS 4,180

JUPITER 86,000

of Copernicus' birth, to 1727, when Newton died. Their work in making the solar system comprehensible is a remarkable story of the ingenuity and drive of the human spirit.

At the time of Copernicus, leading European astronomers accepted the idea that the earth was a ball positioned in space and recognized that the sun, the moon, and the other planets were similar balls. But they regarded the earth as fixed in the center of a structured cosmos, as set down by Aristotle, and envisioned the other planets moving in small circles, or epicycles, within larger circles. This idea of a series of wheels within wheels was systematized from previous knowledge by Ptolemy, an astute mathematician from Alexandria, in the second century A.D. Ptolemaic cosmology offered an acceptable model of the universe, and for thirteen centuries his encyclopedic work, the *Almagest* (Arabic for "the greatest"), remained the astronomer's standard text.

The first man to make a serious attack on the Ptolemaic system was Canon Niklas Koppernigk of Poland, better known by his Latin name, Copernicus. Born in 1473, Copernicus was a trained churchman, a doctor, a lawyer, and, at times, a diplomat. But his greatest interest from his student days at Krakow was astronomy, and at an early age he felt that Ptolemy was wrong. In his view, the apparent circling of the stars around the earth, the movement of the sun across the sky, and the back and forth movements of the planets were due to the earth rotating on its axis. Not only was the earth a rotating sphere but it moved around the sun, which was the center of the

planetary system and therefore of the universe.

Copernicus did far more than revive the long-ignored ideas of Aristarchus of Samos; he determined the positions of the five known planets in relation to the sun and calculated their orbital periods. He arranged these motions in a harmonious system which, as he put it, explained "the entire structure of the universe and the entire ballet of the planets."

Copernicus did not question the circular motions that Ptolemy had ascribed to the planets. After all, circular motion was perfect motion. Nevertheless, Copernicus knew his theory—especially the idea of a moving earth—would be considered heretical. It conflicted with passages in the Scriptures, such as Joshua commanding the sun (and not the earth) to stand still, and denied man's exalted station at the center of the universe. But his book, *De Revolutionibus Orbium Celestium*, was not published in its entirety until 1543, when he lay on his deathbed. It was dedicated to Pope Paul III, and a Lutheran clergyman anonymously added an apologetic preface, which stated that the central idea was really a mathematical fiction, created as a practical tool for astronomers, a series of hypotheses to be placed "alongside older hypotheses which are no more probable."

Either the preface was not needed, or else it worked too well. The book was not taken seriously until half a century later, when the work of Galileo and Kepler called attention to the book that had inspired them. In 1616 Copernicus' book was placed in the Catholic Index of Prohibited Books; there it remained, with works by Galileo and Kepler, until the early

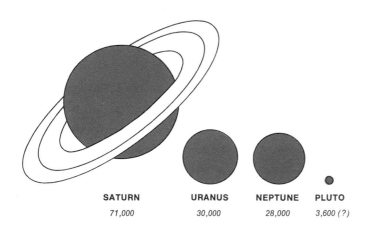

SATURN
71,000

URANUS
30,000

NEPTUNE
28,000

PLUTO
3,600 (?)

*The basics of planetary astronomy begin with visualizing the immense diameters of the planets and their great distances from the sun. At left, the sizes of the planets (but not their distances) are diagramed in relation to a section of the sun. If the solar system were represented by the United States, with the sun at New York, the orbits of the inner planets would lie no farther than Philadelphia. The orbit of Pluto, the most distant outer planet, would cross San Francisco.*

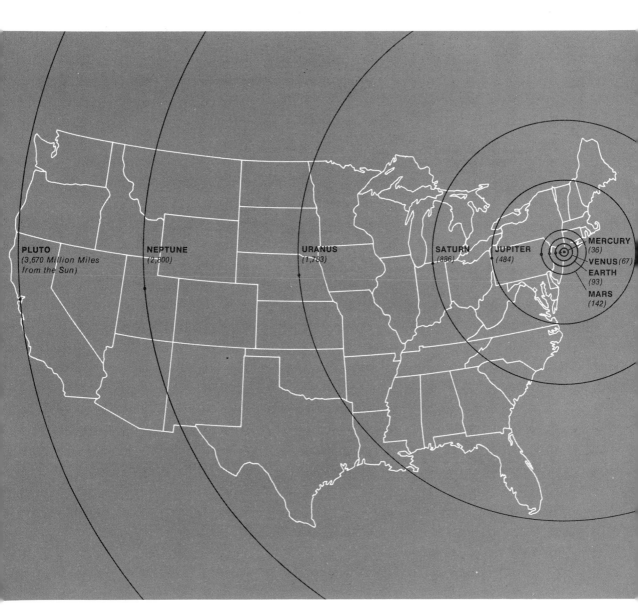

PLUTO
(3,670 Million Miles from the Sun)

NEPTUNE
(2,800)

URANUS
(1,783)

SATURN
(886)

JUPITER
(484)

MERCURY
(36)

VENUS (67)

EARTH
(93)

MARS
(142)

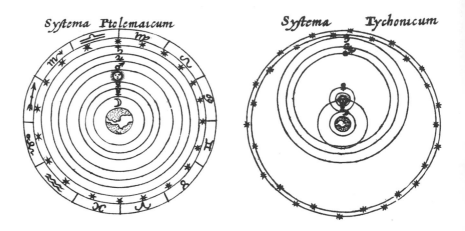

nineteenth century, a more enlightened era.

For all its eventual impact, *De Revolutionibus*, like so many important science books, was hardly a best seller; it was reprinted four times in four hundred years. On the other hand, several conventional but popular books on physics and astronomy written during the late sixteenth century went through numerous editions.

Little is known of Copernicus' activities and early formulations, but when he was canon of Frauenburg he made various observations that he later added to those inherited from the ancient astronomers to determine the elements of his planetary theory. He worked with modest instruments, more modest indeed than the best available at the time, which limited the accuracy of his observations.

Tycho Brahe, on the other hand, who lived from 1546 to 1601, was a thorough observer, the first great astronomer in the modern sense, whose own concept of the solar system—a compromise between the Ptolemaic and Copernican systems—convinced almost no one and did not offend the Church authorities. It is interesting to note that Tycho always wrote admiringly of Copernicus although he proposed many arguments counter to Copernican theory. He was a colorful, tempestuous nobleman who began his pursuit of astronomy at an early age. When he was twenty, he lost his nose in a bloody duel and for the rest of his life wore an artificial nose made of copper, which he enjoyed removing and polishing in front of his associates while they stared transfixed. (Tycho's nose was subsequently said to have been made of gold or silver, and in 1901

his body was exhumed in Prague by civic officials; the greenish stain typical of oxidized copper that was found on the skull may have disappointed treasure seekers, but it settled the matter for history.)

Despite his abrasive personality, Tycho gained the favor of King Frederick II of Denmark, who built him an expensive observatory on the island of Hven, north of Copenhagen. Tycho named it the Castle of the Heavens and boasted that it had cost the king a ton of gold. In the lavish setting of its formal gardens he erected highly accurate instruments for his time (though no telescope, for it was not yet invented) and for twenty years he made patient and skillful observations of the celestial bodies. He published a catalogue, the result of fourteen years of careful observations, that fixed the position of 777 stars. This was an accomplishment of enormous importance to solar system astronomy, for it refined the work of Ptolemy and others and improved the definition of the tapestry of stars against which the location of orbiting planets could be pinpointed. Tycho's observations led to more accurate prediction of the motions of the sun, moon, and planets, an achievement which enabled a generation of astronomers to proceed productively.

Tycho's generous patron died in 1588, and his successor, Christian IV, grew impatient with Tycho's lavish spending and constant quarreling. He transferred to the protection of Emperor Rudolf II, Hapsburg ruler of the Holy Roman Empire, a man of erratic passions for science and pseudoscience. Rudolf appreciated an astronomer who was also an alchemist and

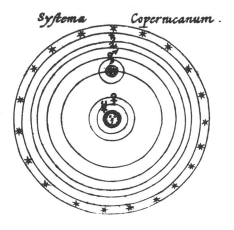

*Syſtema   Copernicanum.*

*The planetary systems postulated by Ptolemy, Tycho Brahe, and Copernicus are shown in 17th-century diagrams. In the long-accepted Ptolemaic model (far left) the earth is circled by the sun and planets. Copernicus (below) published his heliocentric theory (near left) in 1543, but his work was not accepted for half a century. Even then, Tycho tried to reconcile both theories by indicating that other planets circle the sun (center) but that the earth remains the center of the universe.*

astrologer, and Tycho was given a small observatory in a castle near Prague. It was here that he took on a young assistant named Johannes Kepler, and their brief association—Tycho died eighteen months later—was to leave an indelible imprint on planetary astronomy.

Unlike Tycho, Kepler planned a career, not in astronomy, but in the Lutheran church. In 1594, at the age of twenty-three, however, he was persuaded to abandon the ministry and accept a modest post teaching science and mathematics at Graz. He spent more time in astrological calculation, in fact, than in observation of the heavens, and he cast the horoscopes of the emperor and other important personages of the period.

Kepler suffered from polyopia, an eye affliction that causes multiple images. Unable to observe effectively himself, he pored through Tycho's extensive records in the hope of finding regularities in them. Using Tycho's observations of Mars, he set out to calculate that planet's orbit according to Copernican theory; after five hundred pages of ponderous calculation and, so he claimed, two years of effort, he discovered a discrepancy between theory and observation. It was a small error, but Kepler was prepared to discard preconceptions to find it. Years of wrestling with Tycho's data did not make him lose respect for observation, however. It was clear to him that the effects he was studying had to be explainable by physical causes. Eventually, he concluded that the planetary orbits were not simple circles, but that they were ellipses.

From his carefully designed Dan- ish observatory (left), Tycho Brahe made thousands of obser- vations without telescopic aid. Johannes Kepler (right), who was Tycho's assistant for a while, inherited most of his findings. These enabled Kepler to puzzle out the mechanics of planetary motion— no easy task, as the time-exposure photograph reveals. Taken in a planetarium, it simulates 17 years of the apparent back-and-forth movements finally explained by Kepler's laws of planetary motion.

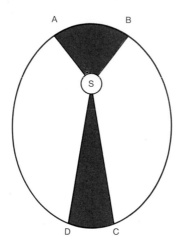

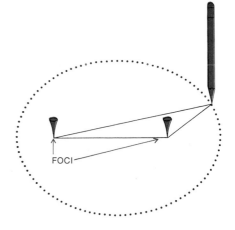

Kepler reached his conclusion reluctantly, for as a devout Protestant he preferred heavenly schemes built on the divine perfection of the circle. But the evidence was clear, and in 1609 he published the finding, afterward to be known as Kepler's First Law of Planetary Motion: the planets describe elliptical orbits, of which the sun occupies one focus.

Irritation over another apparent imperfection of the heavens sent Kepler in pursuit of an answer: Why did the planets move with changing speed, hurrying at one moment, dawdling the next? Kepler perceived that the planets moved fast when close to the sun and slowly when away from it, and, after working his way through murky and often erroneous calculations, he arrived at the mathematical expression of this relationship, now known as Kepler's Second Law: the line joining a planet to the sun sweeps out equal areas in equal intervals of time. In 1619 he published his Third Law, a comparison of the times taken by the planets to orbit the sun: the square of the period of revolution of a planet is proportional to the cube of its average distance from the sun.

Concerning Kepler, Einstein once remarked that "the inner enemy was not yet dead." Kepler's deep mysticism and superstition led him not only to practice astrology, but to seek occult significance in the geometry of the heavens. In his *Harmony of the World*, in which he put forth his Third Law of Planetary Motion, he also set out to relate the harmonics of the planetary orbits to the notes of the musical scale, as did Pythagoras in the sixth century B.C. Kepler believed that the planets sang as

they turned; that earth, for instance, hummed mi, fa, mi. This, he suggested, might stand for misery, famine, misery. He also put forth the idea that there were demons in the planets, and he even suggested, perhaps puckishly, that one might fly to the moon by demonic propulsion.

Amid these bizarre speculations lay Kepler's inspired contributions to astronomy. He destroyed the notions of celestial spheres and perfect, circular motions. And he advanced the Copernican theory by making the sun not simply a center point in an elaborate mechanism but a *body* that, by some kind of force, controls the motions of the planets. Intrigued by William Gilbert's pioneering study of the earth as a giant magnet, Kepler speculated on the nature of magnetism as a force and suggested that it arose from the sun. He died in 1630 without solving the problem of how the sun keeps the planets in orbit. It remained for Galileo and Newton to fill the gap.

Galileo, who was born in 1564, seven years before Kepler, has gone down in history as the man who popularized the telescope and made it an impressive tool for astronomers. This is one of the few cases where a single device firmly altered the course of science and laid the groundwork for a new discipline, in this case, descriptive astronomy. Galileo did not invent the telescope, but he raised its status from that of a curious toy to an instrument of scientific investigation. To conservative churchmen, Galileo's telescope seemed an instrument of godlessness. When he pointed it at Venus he discovered that the planet had phases like the moon, which indicated that it was illumined by

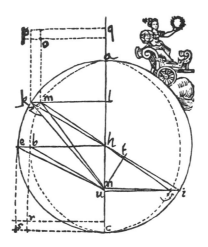

*Planetary orbits, Kepler found, are elliptical (in the shape described at left by a pencil on a string tautly looped around two central foci). The sun is at one focus, and although the planets do not move at constant speeds around it, their orbits sweep out equal areas in equal times (at far left, a planet takes the same time to travel from A to B as from C to D; and ASB equals CSD). For publication, Kepler capped a diagram (right) proving his laws with a figure of Victory.*

the sun and that it revolved around the sun, in the manner predicted by Copernicus. Magnifying Jupiter's image thirty times, Galileo's telescope revealed four moons, and the earth lost its distinction as the only planet with a satellite. Galileo looked at the earth's own satellite and found that, far from being a perfect heavenly sphere, the moon had "hollows and protuberances, lofty mountains and deep valleys," just like "corrupt earth." Then he pointed the instrument toward the most perfect of all heavenly bodies, the sun, and found that it, too, had blemishes—sunspots.

Galileo's observations, particularly of the phases of Venus, lent support to the Copernican system, and news of the findings spread quickly across Europe. But the Aristotelians and Ptolemaists were not to be put down lightly; their beliefs were the accepted dogma of the Church, which was, in the seventeenth century, desperately fighting off the challenge of heresy in every form.

To the astronomer's distress, churchmen denied almost everything he saw in his telescope. The moons of Jupiter? They were illusions. If God wanted us to see them, why did it require an instrument? asked one Jesuit. That the moon shines by light from the sun and not by its own light was, in the Church's view, a direct contradiction to statements in Genesis that the moon is a "great light." And at the University of Pisa, the astronomer Benedetto Castelli (a disciple of Galileo) was forbidden to teach the motion of the earth to his students.

In 1633 Galileo's offense to the Church resulted in his famous public examination and trial by the Inquisition, which ended with Galileo recanting, under threat of torture, his position that the planets moved around the sun. In deference to his failing health and his considerable reputation, he was not imprisoned, but lived in seclusion until his death in 1642. It took the next generation to realize the truth in his views. (In 1968 the Church finally announced it would reconsider its judgment of Galileo.)

Altogether as important as his proofs of the Copernican system—more so in the minds of some historians of science—were Galileo's experiments with motion and the foundation he thereby gave to the science of dynamics. While other science professors were purveying Aristotle's views as indisputable dogma, Galileo actually watched objects in motion and reached entirely different conclusions. His famous experiments, supposedly made from the Leaning Tower of Pisa, proved that, in the absence of air resistance, the speed at which an object falls is independent of its weight. He also established that objects fall faster as they fall farther, at uniform acceleration. Other experiments led him to the idea that later was to be embodied in Newton's First Law: that a body will remain at rest, or continue forever in motion at uniform velocity in a straight line, unless some force is acting on it. Galileo was one of the first modern scientists—the first to deal with motion mathematically and to develop a graphical method of analyzing motion in terms of time and distance and in terms of its component forces. The curved path of a cannon ball, he knew, was the result of a combination of

296
maggio

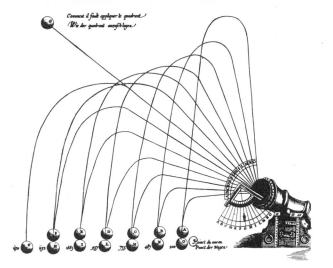

*Galileo Galilei was the first of the modern experimental scientists. His genius embraced the formulation, testing, and explanation of theories. In addition to his work in astronomy, Galileo ceaselessly investigated the properties of motion and the forces of gravity. His discovery that the path of a projectile was a parabola was vital to contemporary artillerymen; they could thus achieve accurate aim by using a quadrant (right). Later it would serve as a springboard for Newton's theories about gravitation.*

two forces: the horizontal thrust of the firing and the vertical drop due to the object's weight.

Galileo applied these great insights to the solar system only in a rudimentary way, but his contributions set the stage for Isaac Newton, who analyzed the gravitational forces at work in the solar system to account for the unceasing motion and the elliptical orbits of the planets.

Newton, born in 1642, the year Galileo died and a century after the death of Copernicus, was a shy and introverted Cambridge professor who disliked controversy almost as much as Galileo seemed to relish it. Had it not been for the gentle cajoling of Edmund Halley (who later became England's Astronomer Royal), Newton might have kept his important discoveries to himself. At the age of twenty-three, watching the apple that fell to the earth and the perpetually falling moon that never reached earth's surface, he sought some universal principle to account for these differences. The result was the remarkable intellectual synthesis embodied in his Law of Universal Gravitation, published twenty-two years later in his great work the *Principia.* "Every particle of matter in the universe attracts every other particle with a force that varies directly as the product of their masses and inversely as the square of the distance between them." From this formula he was able to deduce all the motions of the solar system: the orbits of the planets about the sun; the orbits of the moons about the planets; the movements of the comets; and the ebb and flow of the tides.

Newton based his argument on the recorded observations of Kepler and Galileo, and invented differential and integral calculus to formulate his theory. He found that the apparently very complex motions in the solar system could all be understood in terms of the inverse square law of gravitation. It is a remarkable fact that the universe is constructed in such a way that so simple a formula can predict such a variety of motion on so universal a scale. The philosophical arguments of Aristotle and Ptolemy were replaced by rather different questions, which occupy us still, such as *why* there is an inverse square law and why, indeed, nature seems to be mathematically inclined.

Newton's genius was next bestowed on studies of light and opened up a new chapter in astronomy: the study of what celestial bodies are made of. Early in his career Newton demonstrated that a prism breaks up ordinary white light into a rainbow or spectrum of colors, each one of which represents a different speed of the waves passing through the prism. A century and a half later the astronomer William Herschel discovered that there is invisible radiation beyond the red end of the spectrum (infrared). He then spread out the sun's light into its component colors by means of a prism, and isolated the light of each color to test its radiant heat with a thermometer, which led him to the conclusion that the heating effect of various colors is unequal. His fame as an astronomer has eclipsed his work as a physicist. But his pioneering experiments on the infrared heat rays were important enough to be presented as papers to the Royal Society in 1800. About the same time, the English physicist William Wol-

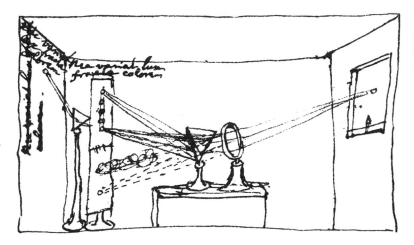

laston, working at the other end of the spectrum, proved there is radiation outside the violet, now known as ultraviolet.

In the 1860's, the great Scottish physicist James Clerk Maxwell advanced the study of light significantly. He showed that light is an electromagnetic wave comprising both electric and magnetic components, and that it is transmitted through a vacuum with a constant speed at all wavelengths. Thus was laid the foundation of what became a major discovery, the electromagnetic spectrum, which ties the radiation of the universe together in a neat system, as the periodic table organizes the elements.

The electromagnetic spectrum was soon filled out still further. Radio waves were discovered by Heinrich Hertz, X-rays by Wilhelm Conrad Roentgen, and gamma rays by Pierre Villard. Gamma and X-rays were found to be waves of shorter wavelength than ultraviolet light. Today the electromagnetic spectrum embraces a widespread family of waves, almost all of which have been used to obtain information about remote bodies that otherwise might not be subject to measurement and analysis.

The discovery that the spectrum can be turned into an astronomical tool was made in the 1860's when the German physicists Gustav Kirchhoff and Robert Bunsen—analyzing how the range of colors changes with the source of light—found that each chemical element when heated to a gaseous state emits its own characteristic pattern of colors when viewed through a prism, providing a kind of spectral signature. No two spectra are alike—unless from objects that are of identical chemical composition.

Kirchhoff also set to work on the mystery that had been created in 1814 when a German physicist, Joseph von Fraunhofer, observed that the sun's spectrum was cut in various places by dark lines. Fraunhofer counted more than five hundred such lines, but their significance eluded him. Kirchhoff discovered that an element will absorb radiation at precisely the same wavelengths that it emits radiation when heated. This happens, for example, to a gas that is placed between a radiating source and a spectroscope; the black lines, or gaps, that appear in the resulting spectrum will be a kind of negative spectral signature of the intervening gas. Kirchhoff thus realized that the exterior of the sun was gaseous, and that these gases were absorbing radiation from the interior of the sun. The black lines therefore became clues to the elements in the sun's atmosphere. Lines also arise from substances in the earth's atmosphere, but they can be distinguished from solar lines. Kirchhoff himself identified several of the sun's elements and started astronomy on the race to identify others.

As spectroscopy developed, astronomers began to learn more about the planets. Sunlight penetrates the atmosphere of the planets and then is reflected to earth, but the spectral pattern of the reflected light is in each case different from sunlight. From those differences astronomers were able to learn about the gases in the planetary atmospheres. With the further refinement of spectroscopy, the onetime wandering dots of light in the sky loomed up as individual worlds that were alive and active—and waiting to be explored more fully.

# 2. THE NEW ASTRONOMER AND HIS TOOLS

An astronomer sends an electric flash through a mixture of gases such as one might find on Jupiter and analyzes the products by means of a computer. An observer trains a laser beam on an almost invisible satellite orbiting the earth, turns a dial, and records the exact position of the object in the sky. With an invisible but powerful burst of nuclear radiation a scientist examines a piece of dark rock that apparently fell from the sky.

Galileo—and generations of astronomers after him—would be astounded if they were to witness these scenes, typical of the modern astronomer at work.

At the Smithsonian Astrophysical Observatory (S.A.O.) in Cambridge, Massachusetts, there are no optical telescopes, and its sixty astronomers do not wait until nightfall to carry out their observations. Thanks to such recent tools as radar and artificial satellites, they can "see" at any hour and through fog or thick cloud. The astronomers represent such hybrid specialties as astrogeology, geodesy, astroarchaeology, and meteoritics, as well as "old-fashioned" physics, mathematics, and computer programing. Most of them have no degree in astronomy as such, and very few have occasion to look through the eyepiece of an optical telescope. Their enterprises include computer studies of the dust in interplanetary space, mathematical investigation of the rings of Saturn and the inside of the sun, and theoretical studies of the origin of the solar system and the universe itself.

Pure science ignores national boundaries, and the new astronomer is a kind of youthful

scientific Peace Corpsman. At thirty-three—
the average age at S.A.O.—he travels some
forty thousand miles a year and may spend
weeks or months at outlying posts in India and
Africa. By the same token, the S.A.O. enter-
tains, and shares data with, astronomer-com-
muters from Greece, Ethiopia, Czechoslovakia,
and Italy. Not untypically, a Smithsonian astronomer welcomes a Russian scientist whom
he had last seen a few months earlier in Mos-
cow. Twenty per cent of the world's astronomers are in some way associated with the
Smithsonian Observatory.

The S.A.O., which was founded in 1890, is an
international facility in other ways. Currently,
its complex of buildings on Harvard's Observatory Hill includes three worldwide bureaus: the
Central Bureau for Astronomical Telegrams
wires announcements of all new astronomical
discoveries throughout the world; the Central
Bureau for Satellite Geodesy provides data
from artificial satellites to laboratories interested in obtaining the correct configuration
of the earth; and the Center for Short-lived
Phenomena monitors and arranges for on-the-
spot investigation of the often mysterious natural occurrences that appear briefly and disappear rapidly.

The man who heads the enterprise is Iowa-
born Fred Lawrence Whipple, a practicing astronomer whose special field of interest includes
comets, meteors, and other interplanetary materials. Since he became director of the Smithsonian Astrophysical Observatory in 1955,
Whipple has been almost singlehandedly responsible for making the observatory a major

force of the space age. In the early 1950's, even
before the launching of Sputnik began a new
era in space exploration, he recognized that an
artificial satellite could easily become one of
astronomy's most important tools and he par-
ticipated significantly in the successful effort
of American scientists to put a satellite aloft
during the International Geophysical Year
(I.G.Y.), 1957–1958.

The principle of the orbiting satellite had
long been known. Isaac Newton knew that if
a man fired a cannon ball from a mountaintop
at a sufficient speed—five miles per second—
the ball would fly out into space and (discount-
ing air resistance) would continually circum-
navigate the globe, held in orbit by centrifugal
force just balancing gravitational pull. In
Newton's day, of course, no cannon had sufficient power or "muzzle velocity," and the
achievement of circular velocity, as it is
known, had to wait until powerful rockets were
developed in the United States and the Soviet
Union after World War II.

In the United States the satellite project
proposed for the I.G.Y. drew immediate support, but it was soon apparent that the actual
lofting was only part of the job. Once in orbit,
a satellite is not only hard to spot, but is subject to the fluctuating force of gravity, the
pressure of radiation from the sun, and the frictional effects of the few molecules of earth's
upper atmosphere. Taken together, these tend
to make accurate prediction of the satellite's
position as tricky as locating a golf ball in the
vastness of the Pacific.

Whipple set up a vast network of Baker-

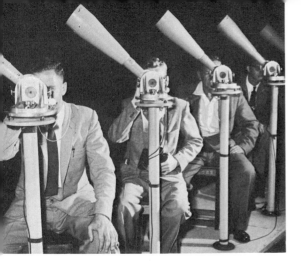

Nunn tracking cameras, with headquarters at S.A.O., which has continued in use ever since the I.G.Y. The three-ton cameras, each about the size of a refrigerator, were designed to work with a radio tracking system known as Minitrack and with the help of amateur astronomers and sky-watchers—an old tradition—organized as Project Moonwatch.

The tracking system, with Moonwatch teams in twenty-two countries, chalks up fifteen to twenty thousand observations each year, and the camera stations themselves make about thirty thousand observations. To see the system in action, let us focus on Cambridge for an instant: here, observations supplied by Moonwatch teams are fed into computers that spell out the calculated orbit of a target satellite—there are some twenty-five of interest at any given time to Smithsonian observers—and they teletype the position to the station that lies next along the satellite's path. There, observers ready the squat Baker-Nunn camera and aim at the appropriate position in the sky. The camera goes to work at the turn of a dial and automatically follows the satellite, swiveling smoothly to keep pace with its motion. Once the position is determined from the photographs, it is teletyped back to Cambridge. Here it is fed into a computer and the corrected orbital passage is flashed in a matter of seconds to stations around the world.

Early in the development of satellites, Whipple saw that they could be used to yield information about the earth as a planet that no instrument could obtain before. The perturbations of the satellite's orbit, for instance, could tell the scientist how the earth's gravitational field changes and in turn this tells him something about the shape of the earth—or "figure," as geodesists speak of it. One result of this was the model prepared in 1967, the S.A.O.'s "Standard Earth," the product of forty thousand observations, which shows that the earth, while closely spherical, is to a very slight degree shaped like an eggplant—with the distance from the center of the earth to the North Pole some eighty feet greater than to the South Pole. Such information not only perfects our knowledge of the earth but aids in the plotting of accurate orbits for satellites.

Laser beams are now being used for highly accurate tracking of satellites, and one bonus from their use may be the unraveling of the mystery of continental drift. In 1912 Alfred Wegener, a German geophysicist, proposed the startling theory that several hundred million years ago the earth had only one great land mass which subsequently broke up into continents that are still drifting apart at a rate of a few centimeters a year. The theory fell into disrepute in the 1920's because the geophysicists could not find the force behind the drift, but additional evidence has recently revived it. Now satellite geodesy may clear up the puzzle—because the accuracy of laser tracking is so extraordinary that it will be possible to find out whether one "fixed" point on a continent is moving laterally in relation to another seemingly fixed point.

But the chief benefit of the satellites for astronomy is the new information they are yielding about the worlds beyond earth's atmos-

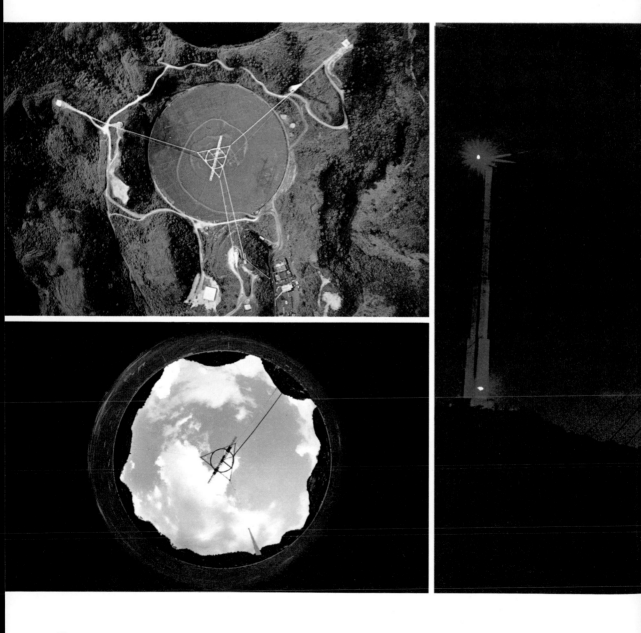

The Arecibo Ionospheric Observatory lies in the hills of Puerto Rico, where the sun and the planets are in a nearly overhead path for part of the year. Arecibo, which took four years and $10 million to build, has been operated since November, 1963, as a radio and a radar telescope. The master control panel is at left. An aerial view (upper left) shows the 1,000-foot reflector, made of 1/2-inch-square wire mesh, stretched above the densely wooded natural basin. In the fish-eye camera view from below (lower left), the 500-ton feed horn hangs more than 400 feet above the ground. The feed horn acts as a transmitter when the radar pulses are sent down to the reflector, which then beams them out into space; the feed horn acts as a receiver when radio waves are collected and then focused up into it. Close-ups of the feed horn assembly by night (below) and by day (right) show the suspended curved track of the feed arm and the movable supporting structure.

*Karl Jansky of the Bell Telephone Laboratories (at top) stands beside the primitive radio telescope with which, in the 1930's, he first discovered radio waves emanating from space. Below is a World War II radar installation on the British coast. The rapid development of radio and radar equipment has opened a new dimension into space for contemporary astronomers. Even with the increased use of such instruments, however, optical observations are still indispensable.*

phere. They overcome a long-standing problem of earth-based observatories. "Our atmosphere may look transparent," Whipple explains, "but actually it is opaque, especially to radiation from space." The way in which atmospheres of other planets absorb radiation from the sun gives scientists on earth information about the gases of these atmospheres, but this opportunity is complicated by the absorbing properties of our own atmosphere. Orbiting telescopes, such as America's OSO (Orbiting Solar Observatory) and OAO (Orbiting Astronomical Observatory), and the Soviet Cosmos-215, are solving this problem from vantage points above the atmosphere.

As satellites continue to populate the skies and we learn more about putting large telescopes into space, the next step might be the space station, which would travel around the earth at a distance of several thousand miles, functioning as a platform for astronomical investigations and an intermediate station for vehicles probing deep space. Once the components of a space station were sent aloft into proper orbit, they could be handled easily, for they would be weightless, and could be put together with relatively simple instruments. Whipple has suggested that the initial construction work might be done by robots—as might the first on-site investigation of the planets.

Satellites are not the only instruments with a glorious potential for astronomy. On a recent visit to Cornell University's Arecibo Ionospheric Observatory in Puerto Rico, I saw what Cornell advertises as "the biggest ear on earth," but since sound cannot be propagated through the vacuum of space, Arecibo is, in fact, the biggest "eye" on earth, a kind of telescope that looks at the planets and stars through a special window of the electromagnetic spectrum. The telescope is sensitive to radio waves emitted by the sun, the moon, the planets, and many celestial objects beyond the solar system. It is also the largest radar telescope in the world, transmitting radio waves to the moon and planets and then observing the reflected radiation. Just as in our own living room we can observe the visible radiation from a lamp or a candle, as well as reflected visible radiation bouncing off the walls, the furniture, and the guests, the Arecibo telescope observes both emitted and reflected radio waves. These observations can then be translated into usable information about the size, topography, temperature, porosity, composition, and motions of celestial bodies.

The huge dish is a wire-mesh lacework 1,000 feet in diameter, fitted into a natural valley. Suspended above the bowl by cables slung from three slender pylons is the 500-ton feed horn assembly. The feed horn transmits the radar signal to the dish below, which in turn reflects it out into space; the feed horn also receives the radiation from space focused to it by the dish, acting as a collector of transmitted or reflected radio waves. The bowl is large because the larger the collecting area, the fainter the signal it can detect, and by moving the feed horn, the Arecibo dish can view as much as twenty degrees from the vertical.

On one hillside, close to the rim of the dish,

I enter the control room, which exposes an impressive array of electronic equipment. An adjoining room houses the computers. A signal is to be beamed to Venus, and one of the operators leans over the control panel to line up the beam guide.

Outside the window one can see the 96-foot-long feed horn move in a slow arc 435 feet above the reflector's center. The operator presses a button and instantly the control room comes alive with the whine of whirring generators. The observatory's powerful transmitter begins firing two-and-a-half-million watts of power through the feed horn onto the face of the reflector, which bounces them in a beam out into space at the speed of light.

At this moment the recorders start to work. The stylus traces a steady, unvarying wiggle on the moving chart. Five minutes go by. Suddenly the stylus fluctuates wildly, showing that the echo has arrived from Venus, a dot of light sixty-three million miles away. The charts are later gathered up and sent to the computer room for analysis.

The Arecibo Observatory was originally set up to study the ionosphere of the earth (the electrically charged region of the atmosphere where ultraviolet light and X-rays from the sun have torn electrons free from atoms) by means of echoes from radar pulses. But its great power has made it more and more a superb means of studying the planets and the moon. On the radio side—what is called passive radio astronomy—the telescope collects sixteen times more energy than the equally famous one at Jodrell Bank, England, and

*The 200-inch Hale telescope on Mount Palomar (right) is the largest reflector in the world. It can view remote galaxies, billions of light-years from the earth. Its scale can be judged from the view at left where a scientist, perched in the prime-focus cage high above the giant mirror, guides the telescope through a long photographic exposure. The telescope's massive mounting might well be described as a successful combination of bridge-building and watchmaking.*

hence can reach farther into space. It has been used to measure characteristics of distant celestial objects, as well as those of the relatively nearby planets. Most recently, Arecibo came into the news because it was focused on pulsars —those mysterious rhythmic pulses that come from the depths of outer space. In fact, two new pulsars were first observed at Arecibo in August and September of 1968.

The discovery that lies behind Arecibo took place in 1931. Karl Jansky, a Bell Telephone Laboratories engineer, was studying radio interference in the atmosphere when he detected mysterious radiation from outer space. Nobody seemed interested. After all, it was thought, there was no secret in the skies that a great optical telescope would not eventually reveal, and the exciting thing on astronomy's horizon was the 200-inch telescope being planned for Mount Palomar. But a few years later an amateur radio enthusiast from Wheaton, Illinois, named Grote Reber built a 31-foot parabolic dish aerial in his backyard and soon verified Jansky's observation. In fact, he found that the strongest radio noise was coming from the center of the Milky Way. Evidently objects in space tens of thousands of light-years away were emitting radio waves. It was, as it turned out, a remarkable discovery—and one that shows that great findings are not restricted to individuals in large universities. Astronomers around the world soon paid homage to Jansky and Reber. As Sir Bernard Lovell, the present director of Jodrell Bank, so aptly put it: "A new window on the sky was opened, with a view of the heavenly bodies hitherto seen

only through the visual part of the spectrum."

During World War II, the British invention of radar opened the new window a bit wider. In 1942 experts were scanning the skies for enemy planes when they encountered a barrage of unexpected static. At first they thought it might be a new German radar-jamming device, or a secret weapon of some other sort, but they soon found that the emanations were from a natural source: the sun. This was the first indication that the solar system gives off detectable radiation in the radio-wave portion of the electromagnetic spectrum. In later years, with the development of more sensitive receivers, radiation was picked up from the moon and the planets, even from Jupiter, half a billion miles from earth, where the radio emission is thought to be the result of fast-moving particles trapped in the planet's magnetic field, like the Van Allen belt around the earth.

In the years since World War II, radio astronomy has become one of the major fields of planetary investigation, and radio telescopes have become awesome structures capable of detecting extremely weak signals. The University of Manchester's radio telescope at Jodrell Bank weighs two thousand tons and is mounted on a turret like a gun, so that it can swing about and track any object's passage through the heavens. Its antenna is a steel bowl 250 feet in diameter, making it the largest fully steerable dish radio telescope in the world. In the United States, the first major radio telescope was the Jet Propulsion Laboratory's Deep Space Instrumentation Facility at Goldstone, California. Its more recently built 210-foot dish

was designed to detect radio signals from artificial satellites but is powerful enough to pick up faint signals from the planets. The National Radio Astronomy Observatory at Green Bank, West Virginia, also has two dishes, one 300 feet in diameter, which is partially movable, and a fully steerable dish 140 feet in diameter.

The huge dishes of these radio telescopes focus the incoming waves in much the same manner as the mirror of an optical telescope. The reason for their extraordinary size is to be found in the difference between a light wave and a radio wave. A radio wave is about a million times longer than a light wave. To achieve the same resolving power—the ability to discriminate fine detail—that an optical telescope possesses, the diameter of the dish of a radio telescope would have to be a million times larger than that of an optical telescope. To obtain the same resolution at radio frequencies that the 200-inch mirror of Mount Palomar achieves at optical frequencies, a radio telescope would require a dish the size of the United States. However, two radio telescopes at opposite ends of the United States can be operated in tandem as if they were two segments of the periphery of a continent-sized radio telescope. Such interferometers, as they are called, are now being actively employed and do in some contexts give resolutions at radio frequencies comparable to the best that can be obtained by ground-based optical telescopes. Though even the largest of present radio telescopes cannot alone resolve detail nearly as well as optical telescopes, they have proven quite useful, and their theoretical limits

in performance have hardly been approached.

Radio astronomy began before World War II, when the British physicist Edward Appleton employed echo ranging to study the earth's ionosphere. In 1946, the U.S. Army Signal Corps succeeded in sending a signal to the moon and receiving the reflected signal. Almost simultaneously, two Hungarian scientists performed a similar experiment in Budapest.

With this striking advance, everyone's eyes were turned to the planets beyond. But the nearest planet to earth, Venus, though four times as large as the moon in diameter, was a hundred times farther away. In 1946, science lacked the equipment to make two-way contact with Venus possible. To give an idea of the magnitude of the problem: one of the first successful attempts to reach Venus, conducted in 1961, began with a powerful beam of 12,600 watts, of which only ten watts reached Venus, nine of which were absorbed and only one reflected back through space. One hundredth of a billionth of a billionth of a watt hit the receiving antenna.

The military demand for antiballistic missile detection spurred improvements in radar. In the 1950's, the improved capabilities of the computer made it possible to merge these two great space age innovations into the Millstone Hill Radar and Haystack Radio Telescope at the Lincoln Laboratory of the Massachusetts Institute of Technology. The Millstone Hill telescope was used by Robert Price and his colleagues to attempt radar contact with Venus in 1958, when the planet was closest to the earth. A second attempt with the same device was

The 19th century was the heyday of the visual astronomers. The Harvard College Observatory, seen in an 1851 engraving, opened a new era when a Boston photographer made the first daguerreotype of Vega, a first-magnitude star. Perhaps no one then realized that photography would eventually transform astronomy. Today the Smithsonian Observatory is head-quartered on the grounds of the Harvard Observatory, and the com-bined forces embrace solar, planetary, and stellar research.

made by Price and Gordon H. Pettengill in 1959.

Although the radio signals traveling with the speed of light took only five minutes for the round trip, the computer and its attendants labored for hours to pick out what they thought was the bona fide signal from the vast amount of noise from outer space. And in fact scientists are still not sure that they correctly picked out a Venus echo at that time. However, by 1961 radar transmission had improved; there was no trouble in interpreting signals, and un-disputed contacts with Venus were made at Goldstone, Lincoln Laboratory, and Jodrell Bank, as well as by a group in the Soviet Union.

The Venus contact was rapidly followed by other radar milestones. At Stanford University radar contact was made with the sun; Arecibo not only contacted Venus, but also Mars and Mercury. From these contacts have come con-siderable advances in our knowledge of the solar system, particularly in the measurement of astronomical distances and of ephemerides—the astronomers' term for the exact position of a planet in its orbit for each day in the year. Radar's unprecedented accuracy has provided the first precise measure of "the astronomical unit," the mean distance from the earth to the sun. The orbits of planets have also been de-termined with new precision by radar, as have the rates of rotation of some of the planets, notably Mercury and Venus.

It would please Galileo to know that despite these advances optical telescopes are still in constant use. Whereas Galileo's telescope had a lens system to collect and magnify light from celestial objects, in the large telescopes of to-day the lens has given way to a large mirror, which serves to focus the light at a more con-venient viewing place, provides less distorted images, and puts the heaviest optical part at the bottom of the telescope, making it more stable. For the most part these large tele-scopes are directed toward the far reaches of the universe and the mysteries out there. The ever increasing size of the mirror means that countless stars not visible to smaller mirrors and lenses can be brought into the field of ob-servation. The Hale telescope at Mount Palo-mar in California, for instance, intensifies the brightness of a star a million times, compared to the naked eye. The Russians' new 236-inch telescope, now under construction, will amplify the brightness even more.

While the large telescopes concentrate on distant celestial bodies, a host of smaller tel-escopes, joined by such innovations as photo-electric photometers, photographic spectro-graphs, and image intensifiers, are aimed at the moon and planets, forcing the solar system to give up its secrets. At New Mexico State Uni-versity, for instance, Bradford Smith has been photographing Venus and Mercury in ultra-violet light. He uses a special photographic plate, sensitive to radiation whose wavelength is just below that of visible light. This tech-nique has been responsible for uncovering markings on planets such as Venus that are missed by visible-light photography.

Working at the other side of the visible spec-trum, the infrared, Frank Low of the Univer-sity of Arizona devised an instrument that detects incredibly weak sources of infrared en-

ergy from space. Low's instrument, known as a germanium bolometer, is so sensitive it can pick up a hundred-trillionth of a watt of infrared radiation—about as much heat as would be given off by a cigarette ten thousand miles away. Among other things, Low has found that the energy emitted by Jupiter is greater than the energy it receives from the sun. The startling conclusion is that Jupiter produces some of its own heat, like a star. The further complications of this discovery are currently under study in several observatories.

No matter how much we refine optical astronomy or how large we make the reflecting mirror, the earth's own atmosphere sets a limit on our ability to see clearly into space. In addition to absorbing electromagnetic radiation, the atmosphere behaves like a turbulent ocean, causing stars to twinkle and distorting every observation of a planet. Satellites overcome these difficulties; so do balloons, much more cheaply. A large balloon capable of carrying a ton of equipment can go up to heights where there is only 1 per cent of the atmosphere left to disturb the view. It need not go very far, for 99 per cent of the atmosphere lies in the first twenty miles above the earth's surface.

The development of balloon astronomy is very recent. For a long while it seemed impossible to stabilize a shifting platform in the thin upper air, much less do it with massive telescopic equipment on board. But the U.S. Navy Stratolab scientists in the 1950's and a group at Princeton University somewhat later managed to accomplish this feat of engineering and to send aloft balloons that brought back some

of our first unclouded views of Venus and Mars. Typically, the balloon is made of extremely thin plastic, inflated often higher than a four-story house, and not only can it hold the telescope and related instruments almost twenty miles above the earth, but, through special sensors, can keep them pointed at the target. In 1959, John Strong, then of Johns Hopkins and now at the University of Massachusetts, sent aloft the first man-carrying astronomical balloon to observe Venus spectroscopically, which provided evidence of water vapor in the planet's clouds.

The modern astronomer also works with a host of tools that are not telescopic but just as necessary in building the portraiture of the planets. One such tool is laboratory simulation of astronomical phenomena. At Cornell University, for instance, Thomas Gold has simulated the surface characteristics of the moon in the laboratory; while at the Smithsonian Observatory and currently at Cornell, Carl Sagan has simulated aspects of the environments of Mars, Venus, and Jupiter.

The astronomical tools of the twentieth century, while revolutionary in their ability to open up new stretches of space, may in the end be as quaint and obsolete as Galileo's telescope when compared to the next generation of discovery. We have already passed the threshold of a new age of planetary exploration in which we can bring our instruments close to the objects of study and land them on other celestial bodies. There, for the first time in man's history, we will be able to make direct investigations—and open another kind of window into the universe.

# 3. REACHING FOR THE MOON

A quarter of a million miles from earth there orbits in stately splendor our planet's only natural satellite, the moon. Worshiped in ancient times for the tides it brings and the regularity of its cycle, appreciated by lovers in all epochs of human history, the moon is at last on the verge of giving up its secrets. One of the earliest speculations was that the moon was a giant mirror suspended in the heavens which reflected an image of the earth back to us. But the lunar features that we see from the earth are not reflections of terrestrial seas and continents. Galileo, the first man to examine them closely through a telescope, found they were characteristic bright and dark features of the moon. However, affected by analogy with the earth, he called them seas and continents (*maria* and *continentes*).

In a modern undertaking of equal significance for lunar study the Soviet spacecraft Luna 3 in 1959 photographed the moon's averted side for the first time. (Since the moon rotates once in each revolution around the earth, the same face is always turned toward the planet. The averted face is commonly but mistakenly called the "dark" side of the moon; in fact, it receives as much sunlight as the earthward face.) Luna 3 found continents but none of the smooth, dark, lowland plains that Galileo had called maria, which are so characteristic of "our" side of the moon, indicating a different geological history. Since the flight of Luna 3, Soviet and American space vehicles have orbited the moon, crash-landed and soft-landed on its surface, and in the near future returning spacemen may be able to deliver ac-

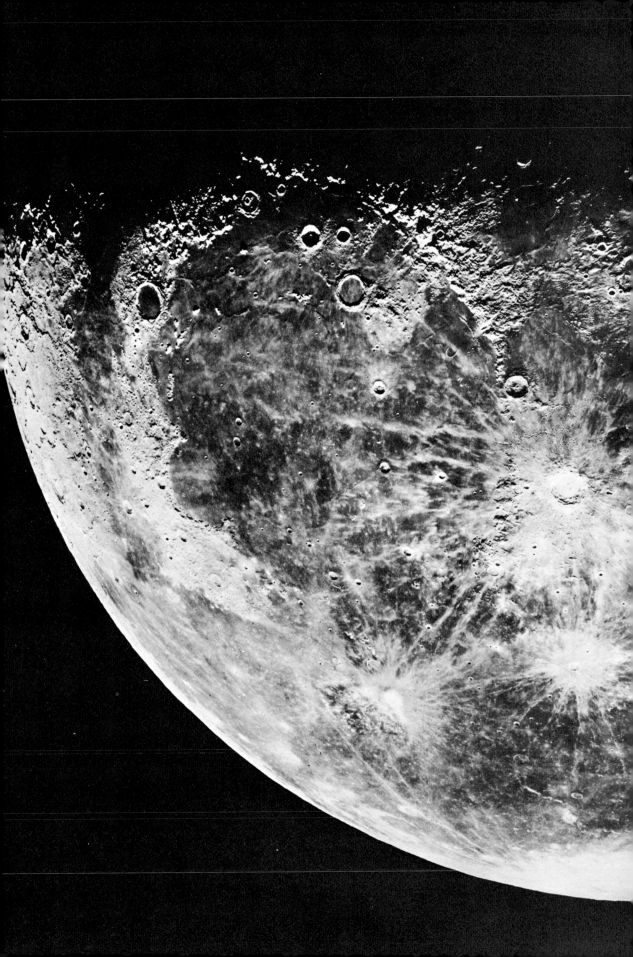

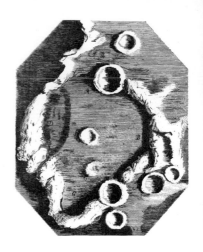

tual samples of lunar soil to the laboratories of earth-bound scientists. We are at the exciting point in history when the moon is being explored directly for the first time, and although many ancient problems will soon be solved, it is almost certain that many new ones, not even dimly glimpsed at present, will arise to claim the attention of fresh generations of lunar scientists.

This exploration of the moon should provide man with a new and unique scientific perspective on the origins of his planet, obtained by learning the order in which lunar geological events occurred. On earth the layers of rock in the crust are a great calendar of past geological eras. The peaceful-looking strata actually chronicle the violent story of vast mobile sheets of ice, of cataclysmic convulsion, and of slow erosion, and they reveal in the midst of these long-gone upheavals the life and death of huge populations of strange creatures that once inhabited the globe. Slowly, as scientists have pieced together the clues in the rocks, we have come to know something of the earth's history —but not enough to answer the perplexing questions of the origin of the earth and of the solar system.

The moon may close this gap. On the moon, where there is apparently very little erosion because earth's major eroding elements, water and air, are absent, lunar geologists (or selenologists) happily see a preserved record in rock of events that took place eons ago. Even the craters that were produced during the early history of the moon still retain the shape of circles; on earth such circles would have been distorted and erased long ago by natural erosion processes. Robert Jastrow, of the National Aeronautics and Space Administration (NASA), calls the moon "a planetary Rosetta stone."

As enticing and important as the moon is to science, we now know enough of its physical characteristics to say that vacationists would hardly find it appealing. The moon is dry, bleak, pock-marked with literally billions of craters, and covered with boulders. Here and there are the few jagged lunar mountains that artists have been fond of drawing, but most of the moon comprises low and gently sloping hills. The surface itself is crunchy and a dull brownish-gray—many of the molecules responsible for the natural color of rocks are destroyed by the intense solar radiation that bombards the airless moon.

Since the moon lacks an atmosphere, it has no weather, and the vacuum is greater than anything we can establish on the earth. Though the moon receives about the same amount of radiation from the sun as the earth does, the absence of air and surface water causes temperature fluctuations from well above the boiling point of water to about 300 degrees below freezing on the Fahrenheit scale in the period between full and new moon. An interesting computation shows that if we could put an atmosphere on the moon like that of earth, the moon's weak gravity—one sixth that of earth—would permit almost all the atmosphere to leak away in about ten thousand years.

This is the broad portrait of the moon, but for scientists the details are being filled in

One of the earliest detailed drawings of lunar craters (left) was made from painstaking telescopic observations by Robert Hooke in the 17th century. It took three more centuries for man to land an instrument on the moon. The actual surface of a lunar crater is pictured below in a photomosaic transmitted by Surveyor 1 in 1966. The spacecraft's shadow is extended at the right. Hooke had correctly observed that all shadows are sharp on the airless moon.

rapidly. The United States and the Soviet Union have lofted a number of spacecraft that in less than a decade have provided more information about the moon's surface than all the astronomical data accumulated in the entire previous history of man. This series of assaults began with the Soviet Union's Luna 2 in 1959, which crash-landed on the moon and became the first man-made object to touch another celestial body in space. Three years later an American Ranger spacecraft also crashed into the moon. In quick succession Luna 9 made the first soft landing with instruments and sent back its close-ups of the surface, and Luna 10 followed with the first orbit of the moon. The U.S. crash-landing spacecraft, Rangers 7, 8, and 9, the soft-landing craft, Surveyors 5, 6, and 7, and the series of Lunar Orbiters vastly multiplied the photographic coverage. The Surveyor photographs have improved our resolution of the moon's surface by 100,000 times over the best ground-based photographs, and show for the first time minute objects on the moon that are only a few hundredths of an inch in diameter. The rivalry between the Soviet Union and the United States continues to provide us with amazing advances in knowledge: in September, 1968, Russia's Zond 5 flew past the moon and was successfully recovered; three months later, the American Apollo 8 made ten manned lunar orbits at a distance of only seventy miles above the surface, and returned to earth after a "perfect" flight.

The photographs now available point up more clearly than ever the characteristics of the two main land divisions of the moon. On the one hand, the relatively brighter, higher ground known as continentes or uplands are rough and broken and strewn with boulders. The Surveyor photographs showed rocks with characteristic sizes of a few inches; the best photograph taken of this region before the Surveyor shows nothing smaller than a mile in diameter. The darker lowland maria are smoother and flatter and more uniform than previously supposed. Several of the maria are nearly circular in shape; others are very irregular. The Lunar Orbiter photographs showed clear evidence of rock movement; in one case, a boulder had rolled down a hill, leaving an unmistakable trail behind it. Perhaps a moonquake shook it loose; perhaps the small particles supporting it were slowly eroded away by radiation or the impact of tiny dust particles from space.

The other striking lunar formation shown in new detail in the photographs is the moon's most famous structural feature, the crater. Of the estimated 300,000 craters that are visible through earth-based telescopes, some are huge, shallow holes in the upland area, as much as 150 miles in diameter; this is ten times bigger than the largest volcanic crater on the earth and big enough to swallow the Grand Canyon. Some craters are only a foot or two in diameter; most are considerably less. Some have central peaks rising from the floor and others show a surface cover that looks like bright spokes radiating outward to a few hundred miles. Some astronomers have suggested that these spokes are jets of powdered debris shot out by the explosion that formed the crater.

In the upland areas there are a number of craters within craters, indicating that they were created at different times, and in the maria there are faint circular features called ghost craters, which would seem to be older than the maria themselves.

How did the craters and maria get there? Until the late nineteenth century, most astronomers thought, largely on the basis of analogy with the earth, that the craters were the product of volcanic activity. Then, in 1893, Grove Karl Gilbert, senior geologist of the U.S. Geological Survey, cast doubt on the volcanic hypothesis by pointing out that volcanoes on earth differ in appearance from many lunar craters and that none have craters as large as the moon's biggest ones. Gilbert argued persuasively that the lunar craters were caused by the impact of meteorites, and in time many astronomers came to agree with him. Today both hypotheses have their supporters, and while advocates in each camp usually are willing to agree that the moon has been the subject of both volcanic and meteoritic activity, they dispute which has caused most of the moon's surface features.

But there seems no doubt that the maria were formed by the impacts of enormous objects, perhaps during the final stages of the formation of the moon. The impact basins were subsequently flooded, possibly by lava, producing their present smooth, dark surfaces.

Prominent among today's proponents of the impact hypothesis is Eugene Shoemaker, until 1967 chief astrogeologist of the U.S. Geological Survey (a position that made him an appropri-

ate heir to Gilbert's ideas). Shoemaker argues that there is enough meteoritic debris flying through space to account for most of the lunar craters, though the fact they are superimposed upon each other leads him to think there was far more debris in space early in the moon's history.

Since meteorites would have struck the moon from various angles, why are the craters nearly always circular? Shoemaker argues that the moon's craters are larger than the impacting object that produced them, because if such an object strikes the ground with sufficient velocity, strong shock waves are produced. Essentially, the object explodes on impact, and this explosion, plus the shock waves, throws material equally in all directions, thus creating a crater that is always circular, no matter from what angle the impact may have occurred. Around the crater Copernicus are many small craters of elongated shape, which Shoemaker takes to be the result of material ejected at low velocities when Copernicus was excavated. Spacecraft photographs have shown similar small craters around the crater Tycho.

Lunar Orbiter 5 data lend additional weight to the impact hypothesis of maria origin. Whenever the spacecraft passed over one of the five circular maria of the moon it sped up slightly, indicating it was responding to a small additional gravitational pull. According to one version of the impact hypothesis, underneath the circular maria should be either the remnants of the enormous impacting objects that produced them or denser rock produced during or immediately after the impact. Brian T. O'Leary,

formerly a scientist-astronaut and now working at Cornell University, and his colleagues have suggested that previously enigmatic features of the moon's shape and motion may be due to these mass concentrations beneath the circular maria.

Although the weight of astronomical opinion is on the side of the impact hypothesis for crater origin, its adversaries account for most of the smaller lunar surface features just as readily by volcanic activity. The spokes around some of the craters, they say, are material that oozed from fissures on the lunar surface. The fact that some lunar craters are larger than any seen on earth is attributed to the moon's low gravity. Jack Green, a geochemist in the space science laboratory of North American Rockwell Corporation, has listed forty distinctive lunar surface features and claims that they all closely resemble volcanic features on the earth. Only twelve of them, says Green, can be explained by the impact hypothesis as well as by the volcanic hypothesis. The other twenty-eight "either strain all geological reason if explained by impact, or are impossible to explain by impact."

Some recent studies have lent additional support to the volcanic hypothesis. Ewen Whitaker, of the lunar and planetary laboratory of the University of Arizona, has made images of the moon through filters that screen out all light but ultraviolet or infrared and then constructed composites of the two photographs. These seem to show flow patterns, for example, at the boundaries between adjacent maria. However, proponents of the impact hypothesis argue that this is not conclusive—some flow of molten material might have occurred as a secondary process in depressions basically formed by meteoritic impact.

A dramatic instance offered in support of the volcanic hypothesis occurred in 1956 when Dinsmore Alter, working at Mount Wilson, discovered a reddish glow in the craters Alphonsus and Arzachel. This was not entirely novel. In 1783 William Herschel noted at least one glowing spot on the moon and identified such features as volcanoes. But he reported these findings chiefly in private letters and the observations, never formally published, faded into history. In Alter's case, however, matters were very different. In the Soviet Union, N. A. Kozyrev of the Crimean Astrophysical Observatory also focused on the crater Alphonsus, observed another glow, and passed this light through a spectrometer. In analyzing this spectrum, Kozyrev became convinced that it was that of the molecule $C_2$, an unstable carbonaceous material unfamiliar on earth but common in the tails of comets.

Glowing spots continued to be observed through the 1960's. In 1964 a search for such glows, known as Project Moon Blink, found that this phenomenon was common, though irregular both in frequency and duration. There is no doubt that red glows occur on the moon. However, Kozyrev's identification of $C_2$ is in doubt and it is not clear what gas he observed. Kozyrev thought that the glows were direct evidence of volcanic activity, perhaps due to molten lava, and that the gas he had observed had welled up from the moon's interior.

But there are other possible explanations for the glow, such as rock fluorescence, stimulated by bombardment of solar X-rays and protons.

Controversy has also been sparked by the long lunar fissures called rills that wind sinuously across the moonscape for distances as great as one hundred miles. One group of astronomers suggests that they must have arisen out of some lunar activity such as a moonquake; others agree with Harvard's William Pickering, who in 1903 suggested the fissures might indeed be what they resemble: dried-out stream beds. Until recently Pickering's idea was generally shunned by serious investigators, but now some eminent scientists, including Harold C. Urey and Donald Menzel, have concluded that these clefts may well be the remains of streams. Whatever atmosphere the moon has is so diffuse that a pool of liquid water would evaporate almost instantly. But frozen water could exist in the cold lunar subsurface as hoarfrost. Liquid water might be trapped below the hoarfrost layer. A meteorite hitting the moon could have ruptured the hoarfrost layer, three U.C.L.A. scientists have suggested, releasing enough water to flood the crater and flow down the outside slopes as rivers. In the intense cold of the long lunar nights, the surface of the rivers would quickly turn to ice, giving a protective blanket to the liquid water carving the rills below.

If these ideas of water on the moon should turn out to be true, then the belief in the past existence of life on our satellite—now regarded as highly unlikely—might be revived. In fact, Rand Corporation scientist John Gilvarry has stated flatly that the astronauts who visit the moon will find fossils of algae and other simple life forms below the moon's surface. He attributes the dark color of the maria to organic matter charred by the impact of protons from the sun. At the moment, however, Gilvarry's idea has few advocates.

The structure of the lunar soil has come in for special attention in recent years—especially since it is important to know whether a heavy manned spacecraft can land safely on the surface. In 1956, after studying ground-based photos of the moon, Thomas Gold, now at Cornell University, was struck by indications of erosion and downhill movement on the airless and apparently waterless moon. He suggested that the moon and particularly the maria might be covered with a deep layer of dust and that, in the absence of air, which lubricates the motion of dust particles on earth, the lunar particles would flow downhill because they electrically repelled one another. Several years later Fred Whipple pointed out that in the absence of atmosphere, dust particles on the moon would be sintered, or vacuum-welded, together. In any case, Gold argued, the moon must be covered with dust, produced both by the constant fall of tiny micrometeorites onto its surface and by the pulverizing of lunar rock through the impact of larger meteorites.

In fact, when Surveyor spacecraft landed on the moon and photographed their surroundings, they discovered that the nearby lunar surface resembled "wet beach sand," or garden soil containing clods, occasional pebbles, and fine granular material. This is in line with ear-

lier observations from a number of sources, including radar, light reflection, and thermal radiation, that show the maria covered with fine particles that cling to each other in a complex tuff resembling the towers and parapets of "fairy castles."

In one experiment, a mechanical arm on Surveyor 3, directed by radio from the earth, picked up a clod and squeezed it gently. The clod immediately pulverized, showing the presence of fine dust. This experiment, incidentally, marked the first operation of a device on another celestial body under direct control of scientists on earth, who could watch the results on television through broadcasts from Surveyor's television camera.

Another important Surveyor finding was obtained accidentally. The spacecraft shifted position after landing on a slope, and it was possible to examine the imprint left by the Surveyor's footpads. They had a waffle-iron pattern, which was perfectly preserved in the lunar surface material. Only a fine powder could conform so exactly to the pattern's detail.

It seems, therefore, that the moon's surface, especially in the maria regions, is composed of a fine, dry, sintered dust. Fortunately for man's long-cherished dreams of lunar exploration, however, it appears to have a bearing strength adequate to support spacemen and quite weighty space vehicles.

What of the composition of the lunar soil? Some preliminary data have come from a gamma ray spectrometer flown above the moon on Luna 10 and from an alpha-scattering device that was landed on the moon's surface

aboard Surveyor 5. This instrument attracted national attention because it was caught on its side as it was automatically lowered near the Mare Tranquillitatis (Sea of Tranquility) and had to be jarred loose by the mechanical scoop through radio impulses transmitted by scientists on earth.

The alpha-scattering device was designed to measure the relative proportions of elements in the lunar surface material. Its observations were somewhat restricted because it was sensitive to elements of low mass but insensitive to those that are heavier than iron. The device employed the radioactive element curium, which spontaneously emits alpha particles (the nuclei of helium atoms), and directed these particles into the lunar surface. When such alpha particles approach another atom they are electrically repelled by the positive charge of the atom's nucleus. The heavier the atom, the greater the positive charge in its nucleus, and the more readily the alpha particles are bounced back or "scattered."

The relative proportions of elements on the moon's surface, as determined by this ingenious device, led many scientists to conclude that the lunar surface contains basalt, a dark igneous rock found in the earth's crust. However, several astronomers—including Thomas Gold—have challenged this conclusion, and it is clear that more detailed analysis will be needed before scientists can identify the composition of the lunar soil with confidence. Moreover, we might well expect different rock compositions in different areas of the moon, as in different parts of the earth. Instead of sending remote-con-

trolled devices to analyze the lunar surface, it is clearly better, if and when feasible, to bring small samples of the moon back to earth, where they can be examined with the full armory of contemporary chemistry. NASA, in fact, has plans to do just this—contingent, of course, on the success of the Apollo mission. The first astronauts to land on the moon will collect some sixty pounds of surface material, which will be carefully sealed in vacuum-tight containers. These containers will go through a quarantine in a special receiving laboratory in Houston—jointly run by several government agencies. The goal is to prevent the possible escape of organic matter that might injure plant or animal life on earth and at the same time prevent contamination of the lunar materials by organisms and substances of earth. (The astronauts will also be quarantined for thirty days.) Afterward, the lunar samples will be divided into appropriate amounts and distributed for analysis to specialists in fields ranging from micropaleontology to soil mechanics.

The unanswered questions about the moon's surface all have a bearing on the most intriguing question of all: What is the moon's origin? There are three general theories of lunar origin that are currently debated among lunar astronomers. In the first, the moon is pictured as having once been a part of the earth, which was torn loose by some violent catastrophe. In the second view, the moon and the earth were formed together out of the same materials and by similar processes as a kind of double planet. In the third, the moon and the earth were formed separately and in different parts of the solar system, but the moon, in traveling past the earth, was gravitationally "captured," and locked into a satellite orbit.

One of the earliest versions of the first theory was proposed in 1880 by George H. Darwin, son of the famous evolutionist. Darwin, an eminent scientist in his own right, suggested that in its early history—billions of years ago, we would now say—when the earth was young and perhaps molten, the sun's gravitational pull raised tremendous tides in the elastic earth. At that time the earth was rotating very fast: a day lasted only four hours. The sun's pull and the earth's centrifugal force worked in partnership to cause increasingly great oscillations in the earth. Eventually, these oscillations became so great that a piece of the earth broke off and receded from the planet earth to become its moon. One piece of evidence in favor of this theory is that the moon's density, while far less than that of the earth, is similar to that of the rocks in the earth's crust. In 1881, Osmond Fisher, an English geologist, went so far as to suggest that the Pacific Ocean now covers the area torn from the earth.

Subsequent mathematical analysis, however, seemed to show that it was impossible to achieve the conditions necessary to keep the ejected mass locked in orbit around the earth.

As a result of this attack, the theory slipped into oblivion. However, the notion of the earth giving birth to the moon was revived a few years ago by three astronomers—Thomas S. Lovering, Donald U. Wise, and John A. O'Keefe. These men, independently of one another, showed that the rotational instability of the

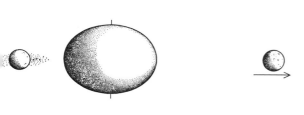

*One intriguing theory on the origin of the moon is pictured at left. Early in its history, the rapidly rotating earth began to elongate in shape (far left) as heavier metals, principally iron, sank inward, forming the core. Just as an ice skater spins faster as she draws her bent arms closer to her body, so the earth spun faster as the core formed— eventually rotating so fast that a piece broke off and receded from the earth (near right) to become its satellite, the moon.*

earth would increase under the conditions assumed to exist when it was formed—that is, when heavier materials were sinking toward the earth's center to form its core. Still, the energy that would have been required for the breakaway is many times greater than that apparently available at the time.

The second theory of lunar origin—that the earth and moon were formed together by accretion from the available solar materials— also suffers defects. For one thing, the theory does not explain why, if the earth and the moon came out of the same mass of dust and gas, the moon ended up with a density only 60 per cent as great as the earth's. For another, it is difficult to see how the earth and the moon kept the critical distance from each other— never close enough to collide and never far enough for the moon to escape—all the while they were growing and solidifying and thus changing their gravitational relationship.

The third theory—the capture theory—is one of growing interest to astronomers. Some calculations of the tidal history of the earth-moon system seem to indicate that the moon was captured by the earth only one or two billion years ago, fairly recently in the four-and-a-half-billion-year history of the earth. This theory would also eliminate the problem of the difference in average density between the earth and the moon. But it presents other puzzles, notably the need to explain how the capture occurred, and where the moon, with its relatively great bulk, came from in the first place. One fascinating variation of this theory is that the moon, larger than it is now, approached close to the earth and was torn apart because the tidal forces due to the earth's gravitation exceeded the lunar gravitational forces that were helping to hold the moon together. Some of the mass landed on earth and became the continents, the remainder staying in orbit. These little moons eventually coalesced into a single moon.

Harold Urey, whose own version of the capture theory postulates that the moon and the earth almost collided and actually traded some material (including water and biological material), sums up the present state of affairs in lunar astronomy: "All explanations for the origin of the moon are improbable."

Regardless of how the moon began, its fate seems tied to earth at least for the foreseeable future. Astronomers have noted, however, that the moon is spiraling very slowly outward from the earth. As one of them points out, the change in distance of earth to sun has been small and remains so, but the change in distance of moon to earth increases at a somewhat greater rate. In due time—millions of years hence, assuming the rate continues—the moon might reach a point in space where it would leave the pull of the earth and truly become a planet of the sun. What would happen to earth without its moon? For one thing, we would lose the astronomical beauty of an eclipse, for there would be nothing around to move between the earth and the sun. The tides would settle down, leaving the oceans less exciting. The nights would of course be darker and considerably less romantic—and poetry would lose its "sovereign mistress of the true melancholy."

# 4.   THE SUN

I f the moon is the easiest celestial target for man to reach, the sun—the center of the solar system—is the most difficult. Consider its temperature alone—an average of 10,000° F. on the surface, higher than the melting point of the most heat-resistant ceramic material developed on earth. In the center it rises to an incredible 20,000,000° F., a temperature that makes the sun a cauldron of thermonuclear reactions, a kind of beneficial natural H-bomb whose enormous output of energy serves to warm the earth.

Because the sun is the source of earth's light and heat, indeed of life itself, knowledge of how it works is essential to man's understanding of his own past and future: how he came to be and how long his planet will last. Moreover, the sun has an obvious attraction for astronomers, since it is the star closest to earth—270,000 times closer than the next nearest star, Alpha Centauri—and therefore can yield information about the nature of stars that would otherwise be inaccessible. For practical reasons, it is also important to know about the sun in the planning of spacecraft flights, since these are affected both by the sun's gravitational field and also by the emission of vast streams of electrically charged solar particles, which can not only destroy the effectiveness of electronic instrumentation aboard the spacecraft, but may be lethal to the spacemen.

Despite the sun's importance, it has long been one of science's most impregnable mysteries. In fact, the nuclear events that explain why the sun shines and how it produces the trillion trillion ergs of energy that warm the

earth were discovered only thirty years ago. All that the earliest scientists had established were some of the basic features of the sun's relationship with the other members of the solar system. The early Greeks, for instance, knew that it was larger than the moon—an insight that required them to disregard the evidence of simple observation. (Today we know the sun has a diameter of 864,000 miles and a volume more than a million times greater than the earth's.) Aristarchus of Samos, moreover, established by geometrical projection that the sun was farther from the earth than the moon. He believed it to be eighteen to twenty times the moon's distance from the earth, whereas, in fact, it is four hundred times as far away. Even so, the projection was a remarkable feat for the third century B.C.

Aside from the discovery of sunspots in the seventeenth century, our knowledge of the sun was little enhanced until the invention of spectroscopy some two centuries later. In the 1860's astronomers and physicists began to apply the techniques of the new science to the study of actual physical conditions on the sun. Within a decade they discovered some sixty-six elements on the sun, two thirds of those now known to exist on earth. One element was mysterious; it had never been seen on earth up to that time, and so it was named helium after the Greek word for sun. Thirty years later natural helium was discovered in Texas.

Today astronomers agree that hydrogen and helium comprise about 75 per cent and 23 per cent, respectively, of the weight of the sun, with the heavier elements representing the re-

maining 2 per cent. Thus the sun, like the other stars, is composed primarily of the two simplest atoms. In fact, contemporary theories of stellar evolution indicate that most of the atoms in the universe are generated from hydrogen by thermonuclear reactions inside hot, "red giant" stars.

At the turn of the century, spectroscopy was augmented by a host of new devices. Among them was the spectroheliograph, an ingenious instrument that can photograph the entire solar surface in only one wavelength of light. With the spectroheliograph, scientists could examine the upper layers of the sun's atmosphere, which could not be seen with the normal telescope because of the intense light beneath the upper layers.

The revelations about the sun's atmosphere through spectroscopy made all the more intriguing the ancient questions of solar research: How does the sun produce its prodigious energy? What keeps it shining? Until the nineteenth century, the best theory was that the force of gravitation was responsible. The sun, it was suggested, was kept heated by its own gradual contraction due to gravity. However, a calculation of the age of the sun on the basis of the energy released through this force seems to show that the sun is less than thirty million years old. This was a long enough period for nineteenth-century physicists, but it was not enough for the geologists and post-Darwinian biologists, who saw processes at work that must have taken hundreds of millions or billions of years.

They were right. At the end of the nineteenth

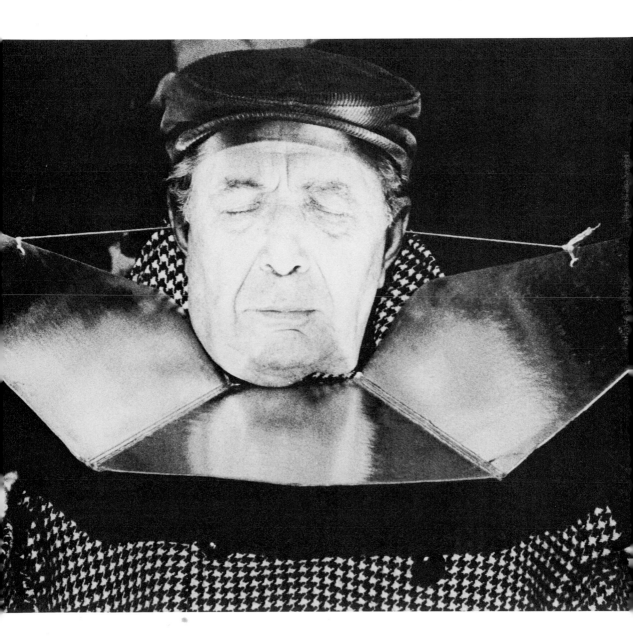

55

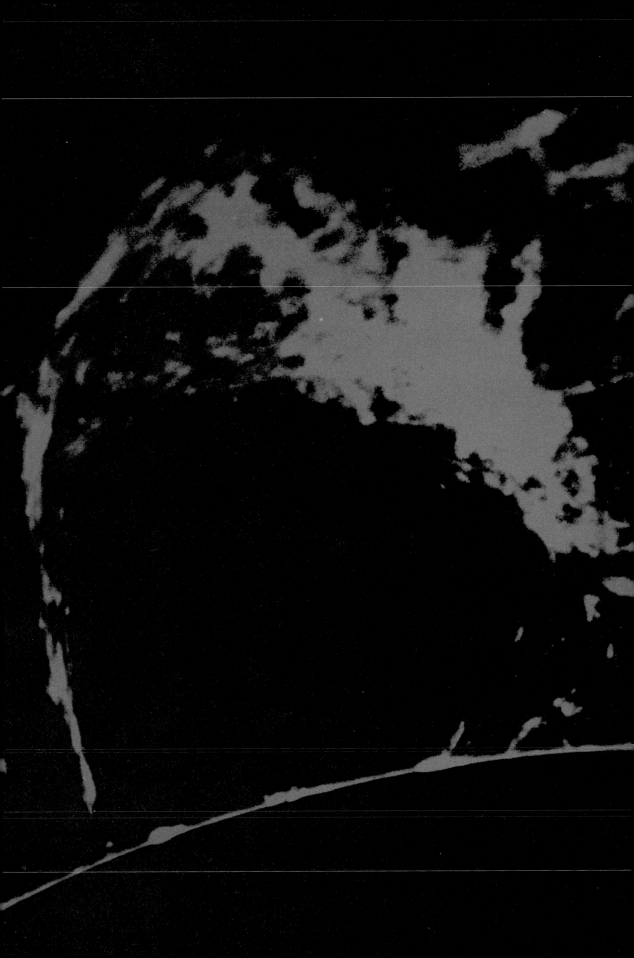

century radioactivity was discovered. This has provided scientists with an invaluable method of dating the age of rocks by determining how long it took for certain naturally occurring radioactive materials to disintegrate. The age of the earth itself was calculated to be about four and a half billion years. So it seemed that the sun must have energy sources more powerful than gravitation. With the growth of atomic research, scientists realized that only in the atomic nucleus was there sufficient energy to account for the gigantic supply from the sun. As a result, physicists and astronomers began to think of nuclear energy processes occurring in the sun's interior as having something to do with the sun's energy. But what were the processes?

In 1938, Hans Bethe, a Cornell physicist, attended a meeting on the origin of solar energy and became interested in the problem. Methodically, he went through the periodic table calculating all the nuclear reactions that might be involved and came upon a series of such reactions involving carbon and nitrogen acting as catalysts that are used up in one reaction but regenerated in another. The net effect of this sequence of reactions was to convert four hydrogen atoms into one helium atom. But four hydrogen atoms weigh slightly more than one helium atom and this difference in mass is converted into energy by the reactions Bethe outlined. A few years after Bethe had made this remarkable discovery (which won him the Nobel Prize for Physics in 1967), Edwin E. Salpeter, also of Cornell, identified a different series of reactions, leading to the same end re-

sult of conversion of four hydrogen atoms to helium plus energy. The energy produced by either set of reactions gradually works its way out from the hot interior of the sun to the cooler surface, from which it travels across space to heat and illuminate the earth and the other planets.

In the 1950's, the development of a number of new instruments made the sun even more accessible than it was before. Motion pictures of the sun in action, photographed mainly through ground-based telescopes and also from balloons sixteen miles up, dramatized the fact that despite its seemingly quiet face the sun is really a surging sea, with plumes, flares, and long filaments of flame shooting hundreds of thousands of miles into space.

Scientists now identify three distinct regions of the sun: the interior; the luminous surface, or photosphere; and the atmosphere, comprising an inner region called the chromosphere and an outer region known as the corona. The interior of the sun is inaccessible by all conventional instruments, and the most accurate method by which we can penetrate its mysteries is by using the tools of mathematical physics. For example, we know that matter at the core is enormously compressed—one estimate is that the pressure there reaches one hundred billion atmospheres. From this knowledge scientists have calculated that a quart bottle filled with solar matter from the sun's center would weigh more than two hundred pounds on earth.

Much more than this is known and can be observed about the other regions of the sun.

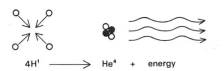

$$4H^1 \longrightarrow He^4 + energy$$

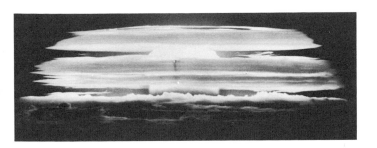

When undisturbed, the sun's photosphere presents a curiously mottled, granular appearance. These granules are the tops of huge rising bubbles of hot gas that carry heat from the interior of the sun to the surface. At any instant of time, the sun is covered by three to four million of these bubbles, which have an average diameter of about one thousand miles (about the size of the state of Texas).

In the midst of these grains there arises a well-known solar phenomenon, the so-called sunspot, a kind of dark eruption in the photosphere. Normally, individual sunspots are too small to be seen with the naked eye, but the largest spots can sometimes be detected at dusk or when there is a mist over the bright luminous face of the disk. The existence of sunspots had been suspected in the time of the Greeks but it was not proved until 1610 and 1611 when four astronomers—Galileo Galilei, Johannes Fabricius, Christoph Scheiner, and Thomas Harriot—all actually saw sunspots in their telescopes and suggested that they were tied to physical reactions on the surface of the sun. It is not known who among the four was the first to see the spots, but Fabricius was the first to publish his observations. Galileo tracked the sunspots and found that they moved across the face of the sun. He thus discovered that the sun rotates, taking on the average twenty-seven days for a complete spin around its axis. The sun, a ball of gas, does not rotate like a solid body: the parts near the poles take almost a week longer than those at the equator to complete one rotation. This phenomenon is known as "differential rotation."

Galileo also found that some sunspots lasted only a few minutes; others live for weeks or even months. The telescope revealed their irregular structure—a dark central core, or umbra, and delicate filaments, or penumbrae, which radiate out from the center like the spokes of a wheel.

Despite these findings, sunspots were not readily accepted, largely because people refused to give up their belief in the Aristotelian dogma that the sun was a ball of "pure fire." It is recorded that some people refused to look through Galileo's telescope, lest they become bewitched and share in the defilement of the sun. Scheiner, a Jesuit priest in Ingolstadt, Bavaria, reported seeing spots and, in fact, using them to determine the period of rotation of the sun and was reprimanded by his superiors for "claiming to have seen things of which nothing could be read in Aristotle."

In time, sunspots became a major subject of study, and today we know a good deal more about them. For one thing, spots are usually found in pairs or in complex patches or groups, which may contain as many as a hundred individual spots of varying size and may extend for some two hundred thousand miles across the face of the sun. The largest spot group ever observed was seen in April, 1947. Its total area was seven billion square miles, or one third of one per cent of the area of the solar disk. This tiny observed area, incidentally, is twelve thousand times greater than the entire surface area of the earth.

One of the more fascinating findings about the behavior of sunspots is that they wax and

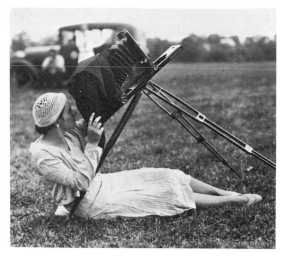

Eclipses of the sun and the moon
are fascinating phenomena for
both professional and amateur
astronomers, who often travel to
the exact center of the eclipse
path, like the quaint group of
Harvard observers (above, right)
seen on an expedition to Kentucky
in 1869. The lady (above, left)
is an amateur, photographing an
eclipse in New Hampshire in the
1930's. At center, an interested
crowd gathers around a French
street-corner pay telescope for
a glimpse of a lunar eclipse.
The special mask with filters (below) was devised in England to
enable enthusiasts to view solar
eclipses in safety. When the
moon's orbit carries it too far
from the earth to mask the sun
completely an annular (or ring-
shaped) eclipse can occur. A
brilliant ring of the solar
disk surrounds the silhouette of
the moon, as in the striking
photograph seen at far right.

OVERLEAF: *This vivid sequence of photographs was taken in Norway during the month of June, when the midsummer sun is farthest north of the equator. In such high latitudes the sun never quite sets, merely sinking low, skimming the horizon, and then beginning its upward path again. The 24 photographs were taken at hourly intervals, starting at 3:27 P.M., with the camera swiveled 15° to the right each time so that the series shows a full rotation of the earth on its axis.*

61

wane in both numbers and strength over a cycle of eleven years.

Charles Abbot, a pioneering solar observer and former head of the Smithsonian Observatory, devoted forty years to attempting to prove that there was a connection between the periodic behavior of sunspots and the weather on earth. Subsequently Fred Whipple subjected these data to rigorous analysis and found that the correlation was only marginal.

What are sunspots? Galileo and Kepler thought of them as clouds of smoke arising from the hot sun. Others suggested that they were "slag" ejected by the sun, so that it could shine brightly, and still others thought they were the result of volcanic action or the sites of great tornadoes, set into violent motion by currents of blowtorch heat.

Today sunspots have been measured as cooler than the surrounding photosphere. The coolness is apparently caused by the strong sunspot magnetic fields, which have been observed spectroscopically. According to one theory, these fields form walls that prevent the hot gases of the sun's interior from penetrating to the surface through the sunspot regions. The magnetic field in the sunspot area breaks this flow of heat, and the umbra drops in temperature as much as $3,600°$ F. The strength of the magnetic field in a sunspot umbra is typically about fifteen thousand times that of the earth's magnetic field.

The magnetic nature of the sunspot was first reported at the turn of the century by the American astronomer George Ellery Hale, inventor of the spectroheliograph, who found spectroscopically that the polarity of the magnetic fields regularly reverses itself with each successive eleven-year cycle of sunspot activity. This behavior is so regular that, according to Karl Kiepenheuer of the Fraunhofer Institute in Freiburg, Germany, the sunspots can be regarded as centers which receive "messages" about the activity of the currents in the interior of the sun. Using the new science of magnetohydrodynamics—the study of the flow of electrically charged gases through a magnetic field—theoretical astrophysicists are now beginning to provide explanations for some of the very complex phenomena which have been observed in and around sunspots.

Upward from the surface one finds the chromosphere, the first of the two zones of the solar atmosphere. The chromosphere is an unstable, turbulent region some five to ten thousand miles deep. It looks somewhat like a burning prairie, with jets of flame leaping up from it in all directions. These jets are called spicules (from the Latin word for spike); they shoot out to a height of ten thousand miles at a speed of fifteen to twenty miles per second. At times they seem to remain stationary for ten to fifteen minutes like elongated towers of flame, then topple or fade away. Scientists think the spicules might be a kind of upward movement from the granules of the photosphere, but evidence of such a relationship between the two regions is thus far inconclusive.

The turbulence of the chromosphere is shown most spectacularly by the well-known solar flare, a huge tongue of intensely bright flame that develops suddenly as a result of violent

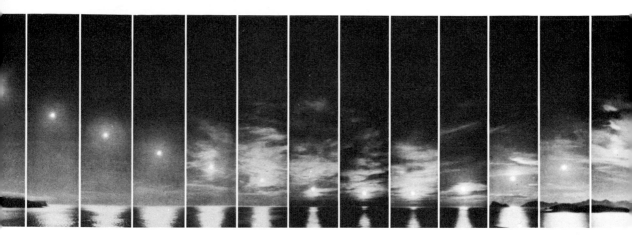

interactions between intense electromagnetic forces near sunspots. These flares can be relatively small, or they can protrude tens of thousands of miles. When a flare occurs, there is a large emission of all kinds of radiation, which affects our ionosphere and our communications. X-rays were first detected in solar flares in 1956 by instruments carried to high altitudes by a device developed by James Van Allen of the University of Iowa and known as a rockoon. This device was a marriage of a rocket and a balloon; the balloon carried a number of small rockets aloft, and these were fired to the same altitude a ground-based rocket would have achieved at far greater expense.

Solar flares also give rise to other phenomena of importance on earth. Solar flare events emit charged particles that travel outward from the sun. When they reach the earth itself they disturb the earth's magnetic field and charged particles enter our atmosphere to create spectacular auroras in the night sky. Flares also send out radio waves and cosmic rays. The number of flares, like the number of sunspots, varies sharply during the eleven-year solar activity cycle. Because of the hazard of cosmic rays from flares, Russian and American officials always consult a number of solar observatories for flare danger predictions before approving a space flight.

Another marked upheaval of the chromosphere is known as a prominence, a plume or arch of flaming gas observed at the solar limb (the edge of the disk) that can extend over one hundred thousand miles into space from the sun's surface. Some prominences develop slowly and are known as quiescent; others are called eruptive and explode into space at speeds of one hundred to six hundred miles per second. Prominences are most active at the time of sunspot activity, and they typically have temperatures of about 20,000° F. They can be seen clearly when the sun is eclipsed by the moon; otherwise they are hidden from view by the brightness of the photosphere, unless observed with the aid of a spectroheliograph or filters that pass only the light of a special suitable spectral line. When prominences are seen on the disk of the sun, they are called filaments; they look like black threads and usually extend for from one to two hundred thousand miles.

At some point in its growth the quiescent prominence is likely to become an eruptive one and goes through the explosive phase already described. A prominence may also sink back into the chromosphere with equally explosive suddenness. When it does, however, a new prominence is often formed at the point where it disappeared, a sort of splash. The base of the arch that comprises the prominence is rooted in areas of the chromosphere where the strong magnetic fields exist. In particular, one especially beautiful type of prominence, the loop prominence, has its base in a sunspot region. The shape of the loop is thought to follow the sunspot's magnetic lines of force, the same types of lines of force that are visible when iron filings are distributed near a bar magnet.

The outer zone of the solar atmosphere, or corona, has been particularly challenging to astronomers. The earliest observers carried on their work by observing the sun directly (a

dangerous procedure that may have caused
Galileo's later blindness). Subsequent observations—as, for example, of sunspots—have
been performed by projecting the image of the
sun and viewing the projection, in safety. Until this century, however, astronomers had no
way of observing the corona, except during an
eclipse, when the photosphere was blacked out.
Countless expeditions were organized to send
astronomers all over the world to catch the
few seconds or minutes of an eclipse when they
could observe the corona. From such pieces of
information, patiently strung together, a portrait of the corona was developed. In 1930 the
Frenchman Bernard Lyot invented the coronagraph, which artificially eclipsed the sun and
permitted the first observations of the corona
without a natural eclipse. This started a wave
of research on the corona.

In recent years solar physicists have discovered that the temperature of the inner
corona is perhaps 2,000,000° F. The chromosphere, which is close to the intensely hot surface of the sun, is itself only 20,000° F., and
there remains the mystery of why the temperature changes so incredibly at the interface.
The general feeling among scientists is that
the heat arises from shock waves created as
a result of the tremendously fast movement of
jets of gas arising from the interior.

Spacecraft and radio experiments have also
enabled astronomers to explore another strange
phenomenon of the sun, which has a bearing on
earth. This is the action of the solar wind, an
accumulation of electrically charged particles,
mainly protons and electrons, that stream from

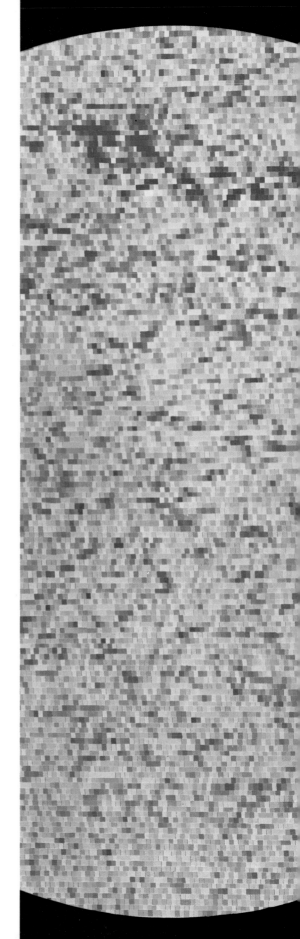

the corona at tremendous speed (a million miles per hour) far out into the solar system. As it travels, the solar wind develops a huge shock front that compresses the earth's magnetosphere, or magnetic envelope, into an elongated teardrop shape, whose blunt end is within forty thousand miles of the earth's surface and whose other end tapers outward four million miles on the dark side of the earth. Occasional violent events on the sun, such as solar flares, greatly increase the flux of these charged particles, creating havoc with communications on the earth and posing a potential threat to spacemen.

The solar wind is responsible for other curious effects. Using data from the radio telescope at Arecibo, Edwin Salpeter and his colleagues have investigated the twinkling, or scintillation, of radio stars and have found it is caused by irregularities in the solar wind. The scientists uncovered a direct relationship between the distribution of turbules (clots of solar wind material), their velocity, and the size of the radio sources. When there were solar flares shooting into space, the twinkling increased. By monitoring the scintillation, scientists can now plot the passage of the turbules as the plasma moves from the sun.

Astronomers today do not generally agree on how the sun was born and how it will die. One popular view, however, is as follows: five billion years ago the sun emerged out of a stray cloud of hydrogen gas, similar to wisps of gas that are seen today in the Milky Way. The particles of this particular primordial gas condensed in time into the protosun, a primitive precursor of our sun, which swirled inside a rotating disk, much larger than the present sun. Within this disk local concentrations of matter grew in size and eventually became planets. Meanwhile, as the sun continued to condense, the increasing rate of collision among the atoms in its interior raised the temperatures. When the interior temperatures reached about 2,000,000° F., thermonuclear reactions began. Soon the sun ceased contracting; a star was born.

As the sun continues to convert hydrogen into helium, it slowly sets into operation the mechanism by which the sun will eventually die. This will not take place for another several billion years, allowing man enough time, it would seem, to prepare for that awesome event.

At that time all the hydrogen in the hot interior will be used up and the sun will continue its earlier gravitational contraction. As the inside becomes hotter, the theory of stellar evolution predicts that the sun's surface will cool and swell, growing into a red giant that will engulf Mercury and probably Venus, too. Its intense heat will make the earth's oceans boil. As the solar internal temperatures increase, the helium ash will be utilized as fuel and a brief period of stability will be imparted to the sun. But despite such stable interludes, the sun will inexorably evolve into a state of greater and greater gravitational collapse until it becomes a white dwarf, an incredibly dense star the size of a planet. In time the white dwarf will cool and the sun will become a lifeless black dwarf—a star corpse, one of many in the cemetery of the universe.

The Kitt Peak solar telescope
near Tucson (above), the largest
in the world, was dedicated in
1962. Atop the permanent vertical column, 110 feet high, is a
flat, 80-inch mirror (near right).
The mirror is movable so that it
can continually follow the sun
despite the earth's rotation.
From its changing position, the
mirror reflects sunlight 480
feet southward down a slanting
optical tunnel to a 60-inch long-
focus mirror set deep in the
ground. The intense light beam
(below) is then reflected upward
280 feet to a 48-inch mirror that
focuses light into the observing
room. Here, still below ground,
the solar disk is projected onto
a 34-inch-wide light table (far
right), where it can be examined
through spectrographic filters.

# 5. VENUS: EARTH'S MYSTERIOUS TWIN

From the sun to Pluto, the farthest planet, the solar system stretches almost four billion miles. The intervening space is filled with objects that can be conveniently divided into three categories: the terrestrial planets (Mercury, Venus, the earth, and Mars) and their moons, the Jovian planets (Jupiter, Saturn, Uranus, and Neptune) and their moons, and the objects that occupy interplanetary space (asteroids, comets, and miscellaneous debris). The terrestrial (or inner) planets are not only roughly comparable in size—ranging from about 3,000 to 7,900 miles in diameter—but they seem to be basically alike in chemical composition, if not in physical setting. The Jovians, on the other hand, are giant worlds far less dense than the terrestrial planets.

Of the inner planets, Venus, closest to earth and its near twin in size and mass, has been—quite literally—shrouded in mystery. A heavy cloud cover masks its surface and until the recent development of radio and radar techniques to "see" through the clouds, little could be known with assurance about the planet itself. Even its size was only imprecisely known, and the length of the Venerean day (the planet's period of rotation about its axis) was anyone's guess. Such lack of data left men free to speculate on the "inhabitants" of Venus, and over the years the speculations ranged from a wistful picture of a world, much like our own, populated by intelligent creatures to the more dispassionate view of oceans swarming with primeval organic forms.

Scientific awareness of a potential life-supporting environment on Venus goes back to

Dr. W. H. Pickering (left) is director of the Jet Propulsion Laboratory, which constructed two Mariner spacecraft like the prototype below in less than a year. Each craft was launched toward Venus atop an Atlas-Agena rocket combination (below, right) from Cape Kennedy. Mariner 1 had to be destroyed minutes after launching, but Mariner 2 took off successfully in August, 1962, flew past Venus for 35 minutes 109 days later, and radioed 90 million bits of experimental data back to earth.

The device at right is Venera 1, the prototype for the Soviet Union's series of spacecraft that have made signal contributions to our knowledge of Venus. In 1967 Venera 4 flew by the planet and ejected a capsule that entered the Venerean atmosphere. After deploying a parachute, the capsule floated down toward the surface, radioing back to earth man's first direct measurements of the pressure, temperature, and composition of the atmosphere of another planet in our solar system.

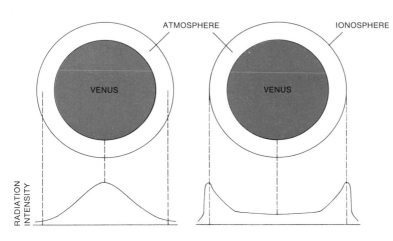

RADIATION INTENSITY

ATMOSPHERE

VENUS

IONOSPHERE

VENUS

1761 when the noted Russian scientist M. V. Lomonosov observed a transit of Venus—a rare occurrence in which the planet passes in front of the sun—and was amazed to see a ring around the disk as it passed one limb or edge of the sun and another ring as it passed the other limb. The ring must be due, the scientist thought, to light scattered or refracted by the Venerean atmosphere. Lomonosov concluded that Venus had an atmosphere "equal to if not greater than that which envelops our earthly sphere." Even the most careful telescopic observations of Venus showed no sign of any apparent surface detail whatever. It was early deduced, therefore, that the planet must be almost completely covered by clouds. Scientists speculated that, since earthly clouds are composed of water, Venerean clouds must also be. Since the supposed water clouds of Venus were much more extensive than those of the earth, it was thought that the planet's surface must also be very wet—perhaps a great Carboniferous swamp inhabited by reptiles. Subsequently, other ideas were put forth: that Venus is covered with carbonated water—an immense seltzer sea—or with pools of oil under clouds of smog.

Spectroscopic studies failed to settle the question of the habitability of Venus. In 1932, scientists detected carbon dioxide in the planet's atmosphere, but no one could find evidence of water vapor or oxygen. The failure to find oxygen was not crucial, since biologists know that some life forms on earth do not depend on oxygen, and many believe that entire life systems on other planets could be based on

biochemical processes that do not involve oxygen at all.

Evidence against a life-supporting planet began to accumulate when scientists applied the new techniques of radio astronomy to study temperatures on Venus. In the 1920's Edison Pettit and Seth B. Nicholson of the Mount Wilson Observatory monitored the infrared radiation from Venus and deduced a temperature at some level in the atmosphere of about −40° F. This is quite close to the temperature expected for Venus: its nearness to the sun's heat is more than compensated for by the high reflectivity of its clouds. But in 1956 Cornell Mayer and his associates at the U.S. Naval Research Laboratory in Washington, D.C., studied radiation of longer microwavelengths from Venus. At these wavelengths the planet emitted radiation as if it were at a temperature of about 600° F.—a searing heat beyond the melting points of lead and tin.

How could Venus be at a temperature so much higher than that expected theoretically and confirmed by infrared measurements? The question led to several hypotheses and to considerable controversy in scientific journals. One suggestion, put forth by Carl Sagan in 1960, was that the atmosphere of Venus acts as a kind of one-way filter to let solar radiation in but prevent heat in the form of infrared radiation from getting out—functioning like the glass of a greenhouse is supposed to. According to this "greenhouse" model, the higher temperature would apply at the surface, accounted for by the heat-trapping effects of carbon dioxide and, it was assumed, of water vapor in the at-

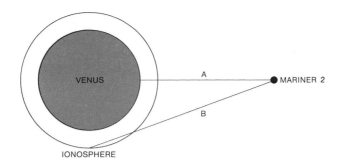

mosphere. The infrared temperature would apply to the cloud tops. A competing hypothesis, called the "aeolosphere" model (after Aeolus, the Greek god of the winds), was proposed by Ernst J. Öpik, an Estonian-born astronomer. This also located the source of microwave emission at the surface but attributed the high temperature to friction from wind-borne dust particles. Both models recognized a surface too hot to support life.

The idea of a cool and hospitable Venus did not die easily, however. A number of alternative hypotheses were proposed, one of them by Douglas E. Jones of the Jet Propulsion Laboratory (J.P.L.). According to his "ionospheric" model, the ionosphere of Venus—the electrified portion of the planet's upper atmosphere—is much more extensive than that of the earth. By comparison, very many electrons are to be found within a given small volume of ionosphere. Accordingly, there would be much more frequent collisions of electrons—and such collisions generate considerable microwave emission. Thus, in this model the 600° F. radiation arises not from the surface but from the ionosphere; the surface, for all we know in this view, could be at temperatures that are much more congenial for varieties of life familiar to us on earth.

A conclusive experiment to decide between hot-surface and cold-surface models could not conveniently be carried out from earth. A simple ground-based radio telescope cannot resolve the disk of Venus—that is, distinguish between the emissions from different parts of the planet. But in 1962 the launching of Mariner 2 offered a chance to perform this critical experiment. The spacecraft carried a microwave radiometer that was designed to measure radiation intensities from the atmosphere and surface of Venus. On December 14, after 182 million miles of travel, Mariner 2's radiometer began to scan the planet from a vantage point only twenty-five thousand miles away.

If the ionospheric model had been correct, there should have been "limb brightening"—the microwave radiation when the instrument pointed obliquely through the emitting, semi-transparent ionosphere at the edge of the planet should have been noticeably more intense than when it pointed straight down, through a shorter path of emitting ionosphere, toward the center of the disk. On the other hand, if the surface were the source of the microwave emission and the atmosphere and clouds were partially transparent, then more intense radiation should have been seen at the center of the disk than when pointing obliquely through a longer path of cool, absorbent substances toward the planet's limb. In fact, the microwave radiometer on Mariner 2 showed unmistakably such "limb darkening," providing damaging evidence against the ionospheric model and leaving a reasonably clear field to its chief competitors, the hot-surface models.

Further evidence came in October, 1967, when the Soviet Union's Venera 4 approached the dark side of Venus and ejected a capsule that sent back temperature, pressure, and composition readings as it gently floated, on a parachute tether, toward the surface. Its last temperature communication was more than

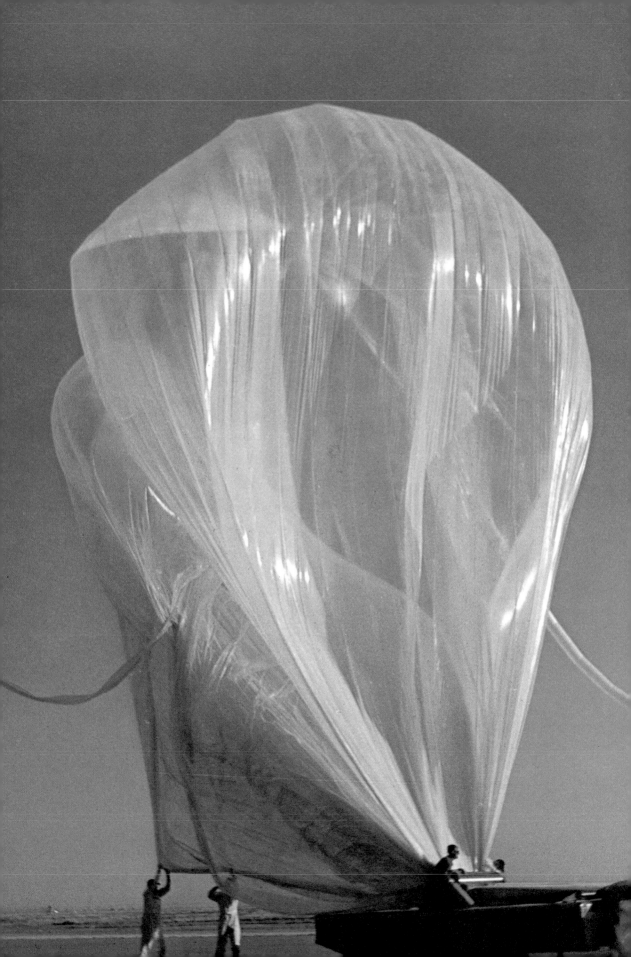

600° F. It is not yet clear whether this represents Venus' surface temperature, but it is known that the temperatures should increase with depth, so that the planet's nighttime equatorial temperatures must be in excess of 600° F. This means Venus is far too hot to support familiar forms of life, even at the poles.

Pure carbon dioxide, although a good insulator, will not account for the severely hot Venerean surface, so to understand why the planet is hot, it is important to know not only the depth of the Venerean atmosphere but its other constituents. If some other material, highly absorbent in infrared light, were to be found, this would strongly support the greenhouse model. Of such materials, water is by far the most efficient.

The planet's clouds are highly reflective to sunlight (mainly in the visible range) and account for the torch-like brilliance of Venus as seen from the earth. What are the clouds composed of? Answers over the years have ranged from ice crystals to formaldehyde polymers to salt dust from evaporated oceans to droplets of oil.

The presence of water—which has always been held to be likely on a planet whose mass, radius, and distance from the sun are so similar to those of the earth—has remained a matter of dispute. In 1964, John Strong and his colleagues lofted an unmanned balloon carrying a telescope into the earth's stratosphere and obtained spectroscopic evidence of water vapor near the Venerean cloud tops. Venera 4 later found traces of water vapor in the atmosphere below the clouds.

The detection of water vapor above and below the clouds, a finding some astronomers still view with uneasiness, would strengthen the hypothesis that the clouds themselves are composed of water, which, because of the −40° F. temperature near the cloud tops, would have to be in the form of ice crystals. Strong has also obtained infrared spectra of sunlight scattered off the clouds of Venus. These show close resemblances to laboratory and theoretical spectra of ice clouds, in which the ice crystals are only about one ten-thousandth of an inch in diameter. Although the ice-crystal theory best fits all the latest data, astronomers admit to a number of other unanswered questions about the clouds. What, for instance, is the light-absorbing material that makes the clouds slightly yellow? Dust, perhaps, but a firm answer awaits further study.

Venera 4 relayed additional information about the atmosphere of Venus, including evidence, surprising to many astronomers, that it is composed almost entirely of carbon dioxide —perhaps as much as 95 per cent. Many astronomers had thought nitrogen would be the major ingredient, but the gas analyzers aboard the Venera 4 capsule found no nitrogen; it may exist, but in an amount too small to be detected by Venera 4's instruments.

Neither Venera 4 nor the American spacecraft Mariner 5 (which flew by Venus thirty-four hours later) resolved a perplexing question: Just how large is the planet? Seen through a telescope, Venus appears to be very nearly a perfect sphere, and astronomers have assumed that beneath the cloud cover the planet itself

$$P(f) = \int_{-f/s_1}^{f/s} \frac{F(\theta)\sin\theta \, d\theta}{\sqrt{a^2\sin^2\theta - f^2}}$$

is spherical. On the basis of radar observations in 1966, astronomers calculated its diameter to be 7,526 miles (give or take a mile). Though Venera 4 and Mariner 5 did not attempt directly to measure the size of the planet, scientists combined appropriate data from the two spacecraft and deduced a diameter of 7,562 miles, plus or minus about thirteen miles. The discrepancy of thirty-six miles was not easily explained away; worse still, when the radar astronomers reconsidered their calculations on the basis of new observations, they increased the discrepancy by another seven miles. Perhaps, they suggest, the altimeter from Venera 4 was working improperly and broadcast wrong information, causing an error in the calculation based on spacecraft data.

Venus' period of rotation about its axis has become known for the first time because of radar's ability to penetrate the cloud cover. In the past, calculations varied wildly, ranging from 20 hours to 225 earth days. When radar astronomers set out to determine the period of rotation of Venus, they enlisted a principle of physics known as the Doppler effect. Christian Doppler, an Austrian physicist, discovered in the nineteenth century that when a wave-emitting object approaches an observer, the waves are slightly crowded together, producing a decrease in wavelength and an increase in frequency. When it is receding from the observer, the waves are slightly spread out, increasing the wavelength and decreasing the frequency. When the object races by perpendicular to the observer's line of sight, there is no change of wavelength—no Doppler effect—at all. The

example most often used in explaining the effect is the whistle of a locomotive: as the train approaches the observer, the sound of the whistle seems to rise in pitch (increase in frequency), then to fall after the train has passed by. These effects work equally well for light, and since the shift of frequency is proportional to the speed of approach or recession, it can also serve as a measure of speed.

Optical spectrographic use of the Doppler shift in astronomy, successful in measuring the rotation of the sun and the motion of galaxies, yielded no result in the case of Venus. This indicated that the planet was rotating very slowly. Then, beginning in 1961, U.S. and Russian astronomers began beaming radio frequency waves onto the planet and analyzing the echoes.

One method of analysis is to measure the Doppler broadening: when a single frequency of radio waves is beamed to Venus from the earth, it is intercepted by the entire planet. Part of the signal is reflected back to earth from the approaching limb (and is increased in frequency by the Doppler effect) and part of it is reflected from the receding limb of the planet (and is decreased in frequency by the Doppler effect). The center of the planet is moving at right angles to our line of sight and therefore produces no Doppler effect on the reflected radio waves. Measuring these frequency shifts makes possible an estimate of the planet's rate of spin, and in 1962, Roland L. Carpenter and Richard M. Goldstein at the J.P.L. concluded that Venus makes one complete rotation every 250 days. Other astronomers, using a modifica-

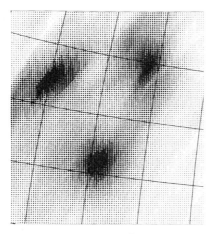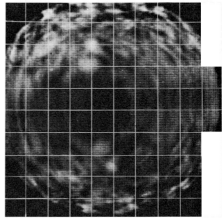

tion of the Doppler-shift method, later refined the figure to 243.

If the length of the day and the length of the year were identical, then Venus would always present the same face to the sun—provided, however, that the planet spins on its axis in the same sense as does the earth (counterclockwise, as seen from our North Pole) and the other planets of the solar system. (Uranus, as we shall see, is a special case.) But the remarkable discovery from the radar data is that Venus rotates every 243 days, not every 225 days (the time the planet takes to go once around the sun), and, most surprisingly, that Venus spins around its axis in the opposite (clockwise, from our conventional standpoint) direction. A 243-day retrograde rotation period has another equally surprising meaning—Venus always keeps the same face turned to earth when the planets' orbits are closest. How the earth could influence its sister planet in this way is one of the most baffling riddles of planetary astronomy, and the ultimate answer probably lies hidden in the very origin of the solar system.

All told, the portrait of Venus emerging from new astronomical discoveries is a bleak one. Because the atmospheric pressure at the surface of Venus is far greater than on earth—perhaps one hundred times as great, the equivalent of the ocean two thirds of a mile down—liquid water could exist there at much higher temperatures. But the accumulated radio and radar observations of Venus now suggest that the average surface temperature is higher than 800° F. and no amount of pressure can hold

water in liquid form at a temperature greater than about 700° F. There is little difference in temperature between the light and dark sides of Venus; the dark side manages to retain much of its daytime heat, though it probably also has its supply replenished by hot winds blowing across the planet.

If the temperature of the planet is as high as present measurements indicate, the prospects for familiar forms of life on Venus are zero. However, it is not out of the question that life forms might exist in the cooler clouds or even —based on biochemical structures quite unlike those known on the earth—near the planet's surface.

Of the many problems that remain, one of the most intriguing is why there is so little water on Venus in any form—by present measurements, barely one ten-thousandth the amount on earth. This difference between the sister planets remains one of the great puzzles of solar system astronomy. One theory is that ultraviolet radiation from the sun has been dissociating water molecules since the planet's beginning, and the weak gravitational attraction of Venus has been allowing the liberated hydrogen atoms to escape into space. Some argue that this process would account for only part of the loss, assuming Venus and the earth began with equal amounts of water.

Whatever the explanation, the dryness adds to the portrait of a planet that is arid and uninviting. Though Venus and the earth may be sisters, born almost as twins from the same primordial material, their histories have been enigmatically different.

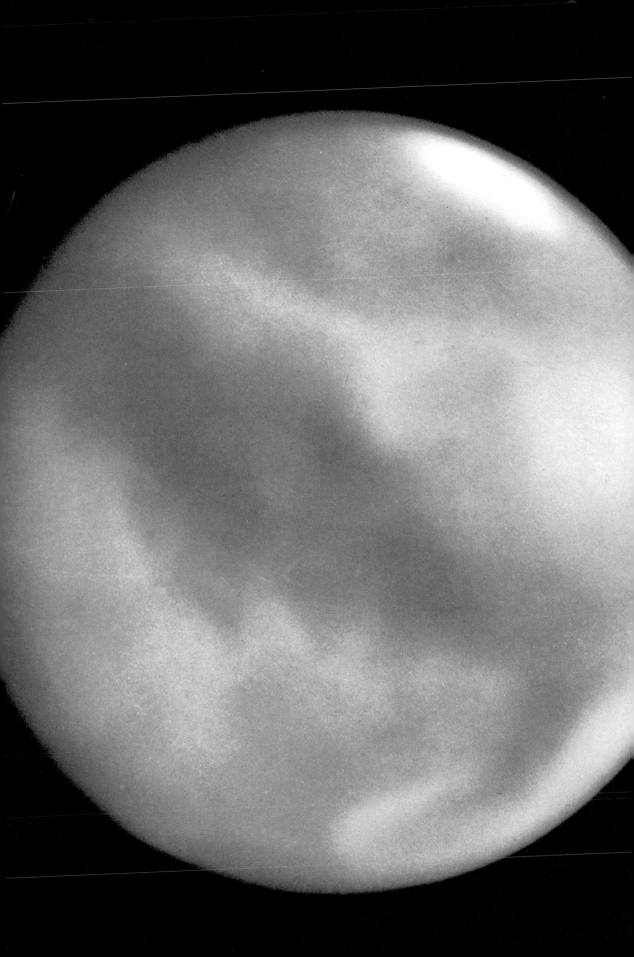

# 6. NEW VIEWS OF MARS AND MERCURY

The possibility that Venus is a lifeless and uninhabited planet has made all the more enticing the prospect of searching for life on the planet Mars. It is a good place to look— as the fourth planet outward from the sun, and only thirty-five million miles from the earth at its closest approach, Mars has surface temperatures that would not be insupportable for some forms of life known on the earth. Summer equatorial noontime temperatures have been measured at about 80° F. At night, however, the temperature falls to below −100° F. at the same locale and season, while at latitudes equivalent to the so-called temperate latitudes on the earth Martian temperatures may never rise above −30° F., even in the daytime.

The idea of life on Mars, especially of intelligent creatures somewhat similar to ourselves, is almost as old as man's discovery that the planets are "other worlds." In Babylonian times the planets were thought to be ethereal abodes of the gods, but not real places. Lucian of Samosata in the second century A.D. was probably the first man to fantasize that a planet might be inhabited with beings that were not divine, and with the rediscovery of Greek learning in the Renaissance came fresh impetus to consider the likelihood of life on worlds other than our own. In 1600 the Italian scholar Giordano Bruno was burned at the stake for the heretical suggestion that God might have shown his infinite wisdom by peopling the universe with countless other beings like ourselves. The most influential proponent of this idea of the plurality of worlds was probably an imaginative Frenchman, Bernard de Fontenelle; in

1686 he revived the theme in a best-selling book that stocked the then known planets with interesting creatures and characters. Mars' sole inhabitants, he suggested, were luminous birds.

In ancient times the planet was identified, not with life, but with gods who were associated with death and destruction. To the Babylonians, Nergal (as Mars was known) was the god of fire and violence; the Greeks called the planet Ares, after their god of war; the Romans later adopted him as Mars, and his symbol—a joined spear and shield—is still used to represent the planet. When the American astronomer Asaph Hall discovered Mars' two moons in 1877 he named them, appropriately, Phobos and Deimos, Fear and Terror, after the steeds of the Greek war god's chariot.

So persistent has been the association of Mars with violence that as recently as 1938, Orson Welles' radio version of H. G. Wells' *The War of the Worlds*, which "realistically" depicted a Martian invasion of the earth, caused panic and confusion in a number of American cities.

The planet lends itself both to the fantasies of science fiction and to the serious speculation by scientists that there may be life on Mars.

The Martian day is close to earth's, about twenty-four and a half hours long; moreover, because its axis is tilted to the plane of its orbit by about the same sixty-seven degrees as that of the earth, Martian and terrestrial seasons are similar in pattern. On the other hand, the Martian year is almost twice as long as that on earth: 687 earth days, so that the length of each season is also twice as long.

During the seasons, however, there are marked changes in contrast on the planet's surface, that is, in the relative brightness of dark areas as compared with adjacent bright areas. These have suggested to some people a yearly cycle of blossoming, growth, and decay similar to that of earthly vegetation. Many astronomers—especially earlier visual observers—reported vivid color changes in the dark areas, a progression from a neutral gray to pastel greens and blues, accompanying the contrast changes, but the reality of this color alteration is now disputed. Brilliant white caps cover much of the area around the Martian poles during the winter, then recede as spring approaches, in a way that seems very much like the behavior of icecaps on earth.

Then there are the remarkable "canals"— the long dark lines that run from one dark area to another. They were first noted by Giovanni Schiaparelli, an Italian astronomer, in 1877 and at once created a sensation. Schiaparelli called them *canali*, meaning channels, but in English the word came to be written "canals."

In the United States, Percival Lowell, a member of a prominent and wealthy Boston family, became interested in the Martian canals. He was a self-taught astronomer but an able one, and a man of considerable imagination. In 1906 and 1908 he published two startling books, *Mars and Its Canals* and *Mars as the Abode of Life*, in which he declared that the canals were inland waterways built by intelligent beings to transport water from the melting polar caps to Martian cities. He believed that Mars was running out of water and the inhab-

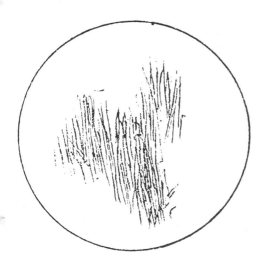

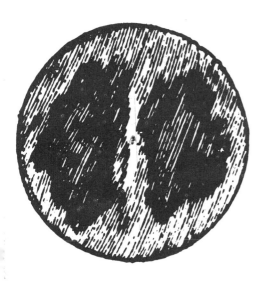

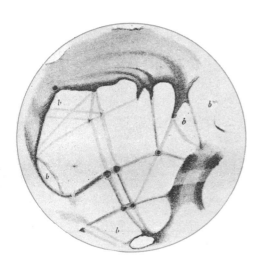

itants had built the canals in a massive engineering project essential for their survival.

Lowell's books stirred considerable popular interest in the "Martians." Edgar Rice Burroughs, noted for his creation of Tarzan, took up the refrain in the 1930's and wrote such novels as *The Gods of Mars* and *The Synthetic Men of Mars.* These invested the subject with a mysterious glamour that attracted many readers, but succeeded in making planetary astronomy disreputable in the eyes of conventional scientists.

The nature of the Martian "canals" is still disputed, although scientists today dismiss the notion of their being irrigation ditches. Even in the best telescopes Mars presents a shimmering, evanescent image, due to turbulence in the earth's atmosphere—what an astronomer calls "bad seeing." Some expert contemporary observers still see thin dark lines crossing the Martian bright areas. Other observers have noted that when the atmosphere becomes very steady and the seeing excellent, the canals seem to dissolve into a mélange of disconnected fine detail. In these observers' opinion, the canals may be an optical illusion—the result of the eye's penchant for order—rather than a true Martian surface feature.

On the other hand, there is some recent evidence that points to canals of a sort. Photographs radioed back to earth by Mariner 4, during the spacecraft's fly-by of Mars in July, 1965, revealed a number of straight lines, although shorter and thinner than those some observers had reported. In addition, Carl Sagan and James B. Pollack have found radar

Mars' image, even in the most powerful telescope, is blurred by the distortions of earth's atmosphere. For years observers have disagreed about what they saw, or thought they saw, on Mars. Percival Lowell (below), after years spent studying the planet, came to believe that Schiaparelli's canali were a network of waterways built by a civilization running short of water in order to transport the spring run-off from the polar icecaps. His map of them is at left. Some astronomers agreed with Lowell; other experienced observers saw no lines at all. Undismayed, Lowell continued to believe in life on Mars and to observe the planet from his private observatory at Flagstaff, Arizona. When he died in 1916 he was buried within its grounds on the appropriately named Mars Hill.

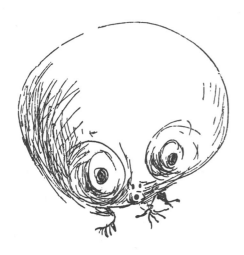

evidence leading to the conclusion that at least some of Lowell's broad classical canals are real topographic features, namely, ridges. In fact, the shadows cast by the lines in the Mariner 4 photographs indicate ridges in some cases, but grooves in others. Sagan and Pollack have suggested that the Martian canals may represent a system of fractures in the planet's crust, somewhat like the ridges at the bottom of the earth's oceans.

Mariner 4 radioed back twenty-two photographs of Mars, representing about half of 1 per cent of the planet's surface. But the finest detail visible on these pictures was of features several miles across. Sagan and his co-workers, examining thousands of weather satellite photographs of the earth that achieved a resolution ten times better than Mariner 4's pictures, found only two or three that showed any evidence of life on our own planet. Nor was there any indication of seasonal changes in the earth's vegetation, although improved photographic techniques should almost certainly be able to detect some of these. Thus, even if a civilization existed on Mars at exactly the same level of technological advancement as ours on earth, Mariner 4 would not have detected it.

Mariner 4, in fact, was not designed to detect life on Mars—nor did it. But the results of its fly-by may have an indirect bearing on this question. Scientists at the Jet Propulsion Laboratory (J.P.L.), watching the computer build up the photographs from code signals received from the spacecraft, were intrigued to see a crater-pocked surface. Although they superficially resemble those of our moon, Mars' cra-

ters are not entirely moon-like: they have a more filled-in appearance and their circular ramparts are often breached or worn away. Clearly, erosion is more prevalent on Mars than on the moon. This is to be expected, since, unlike the moon, Mars does have an atmosphere and water, at least in frozen form, is present on its surface. But is that surface young or old?

J.P.L. scientists Robert B. Leighton, Bruce C. Murray, and their colleagues particularly noted the fact that the number of craters of various sizes detected on Mars was quite similar to the number of comparably sized ones on the lunar maria. These lunar craters are thought to have been formed at a uniform rate since the maria themselves took shape, some billions of years ago. The J.P.L. team surmised, therefore, that the Martian surface underlying the craters also resembled that of the moon in having been undisturbed since the planet was formed. In addition, no sign of liquid water erosion—such as the finger-like pattern of a river basin—was visible on the Mariner 4 pictures.

Their conclusion was that, if the Martian surface was as old as the planet, had apparently never been disturbed, and currently bore no traces of erosion by liquid water, then there could have been no past epoch when there had been enough liquid water on Mars' surface to permit the origin of life.

This point of view has been challenged by other scientists. Edward Anders of the University of Chicago, for instance, has pointed out that Mars is much closer to the asteroid belt

than is the moon. Asteroids are fragments of rocky and metallic debris, most of which orbit the sun in the zone between the orbits of Mars and Jupiter. Straying asteroids impacting on the moon are believed to have caused the craters in the lunar maria. Since Mars is so much nearer to the belt, it ought to have received at least twenty times more asteroidal impacts than has the moon during the lifetime of the solar system.

Anders' argument is that if more craters have been produced on Mars, they must have been eroded far more efficiently than the lunar craters. He concludes that the Martian surface is much younger than that of the moon and has undergone significant erosion. For all we know, shallow seas and rivers may once have existed on primitive Mars, but all traces of them may have been eroded subsequently by wind-blown dust, by the cratering process itself, and by the diurnal freezing and thawing of water, if any.

Certainly there is little or no liquid water on Mars now. In the cold, thin atmosphere of the planet, heated ice crystals would become water vapor, bypassing the liquid stage in the same way that "dry ice" on earth becomes gaseous carbon dioxide. Before the Mariner 4 flight, scientists had concluded that the atmosphere of Mars was very thin, but the spacecraft established that the atmosphere is thinner beyond most previous expectations—about equivalent to the earth's atmosphere at an altitude of twenty miles.

This finding also forced scientists to revise their earlier conclusions about the composition of the Martian atmosphere. Through spectro-

scopic studies at McDonald Observatory in 1948, Gerard M. Kuiper, now at the University of Arizona, detected the presence of carbon dioxide in the atmosphere of Mars. Like most astronomers, however, he had concluded that the major ingredient was nitrogen. But while Mariner 4's instruments showed a reduced total atmospheric pressure on Mars, the actual amount of carbon dioxide present did not differ from that recorded earlier. This implies that carbon dioxide is, in fact, a major constituent of the Martian atmosphere.

Recently, the spectroscopic identification of very small quantities of water vapor and oxygen has been claimed—and disputed—and ultraviolet spectroscopy, conducted during a brief rocket trip above the earth's atmosphere, found negligible amounts of ozone in the atmosphere of Mars. The oxygen and ozone in the earth's atmosphere prevent solar ultraviolet light from reaching the surface of our planet. This light, artificially produced, is used on earth for sterilization purposes. The lack of oxygen and ozone on Mars means that this sterilizing ultraviolet light from the sun will reach the planet's surface unimpeded by the atmosphere, posing a serious hazard to most familiar forms of life as we know it.

If carbon dioxide is the major constituent of the Martian atmosphere, then the polar caps may not be ice crystals but frozen carbon dioxide or dry ice. This hypothesis is not new, but had fallen into disfavor after Gerard Kuiper and Audouin Dollfus each found independent evidence for icecaps of frozen water. Leighton and Murray have calculated that polar temper-

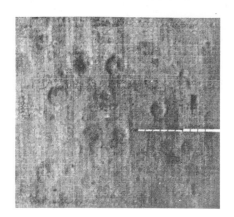

Chesley Bonestell's colorful painting at right, of
Mars seen from Deimos, the outer of the planet's two
tiny moons, in fact combines traditional views with
artistic license. Deimos, only a few miles in diameter, is far too small for us to be able to make
out its surface features from the earth, but we do
know it has no atmosphere—hence the artist is wrong
in depicting rocks that show signs of water erosion.
Even viewed telescopically, Mars' surface features
are more clearly defined than those shown here, supposedly seen by three astronauts from a moon that is
a bare 15,000 miles away. In addition, most contemporary observers see neither the vivid greenish coloration nor the long curved lines that are conspicuous
on Bonestell's version of the Martian surface. Our
knowledge of the planet has been somewhat improved by
the 22 close-up photographs of Mars taken in July,
1965, during Mariner 4's historic fly-by some 6,000
miles from its surface, although, as the bottom picture shows, they covered only a tiny strip of the planetary disk. The photographs did not reveal whether
or not there is life on Mars—nor was the spacecraft's
mission intended to detect this—but they did show
a surface pocked with heavily eroded craters (some of
which are seen in the close-up above). It is still
possible, however, that Mars may support some sort of
life, or may have supported it in the past. Indeed, a
Soviet astronomer, Iosif S. Shklovskii, has suggested
the ingenious idea that Mars' inner moon, Phobos,
which is less than 6,000 miles from the planet,
may be a giant artificial satellite launched by a
long-vanished civilization that once inhabited Mars.

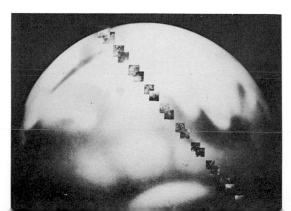

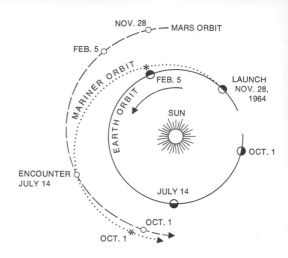

atures on Mars should be low enough (about −210° F.) for carbon dioxide to condense out of the atmosphere, and infrared evidence supports this. Advocates of the dry ice cap do not, however, rule out the existence of ice particles mixed in with the frozen carbon dioxide, and many astronomers believe that ice is to be found beneath the Martian surface in the form of permafrost.

Aside from the polar caps, the Martian surface is divided into two kinds of regions: bright areas and dark areas. A current astronomical debate concerns their relative heights: Are the dark areas higher than the light, or vice versa? In any case, there is quite convincing radar evidence that some areas of Mars are elevated as much as ten miles above their surroundings. These are probably not isolated mountain peaks, however, but more likely large land masses hundreds to thousands of miles across, perhaps similar to the continents of earth.

As is apparent even to the naked eye, Mars is red, presumably because of some material present in abundance on its surface that is reddish. On the earth all the abundant minerals that are colored red are iron oxides, a kind of rust. A natural suggestion is, therefore, that iron oxides are the cause of Mars' reddish coloration. But astronomers are still unsure how much iron oxide would be required to account for such noticeable surface properties. As on the earth, large amounts of silicates should also be present, because silicon is a very abundant cosmic element.

Radar evidence and the way in which Mars reflects sunlight suggest that its surface is powdery. Indeed, what look very much like dust storms are seen fairly frequently on the planet, arising in bright areas and temporarily blotting out dark ones. To raise dust in such a thin atmosphere, Martian winds must be very fierce; meteorological calculations indicate occasional speeds of up to two hundred miles per hour.

Since the winds vary with the seasons—and are strongest in the winter—there is some reason to think that the highlands will be more readily denuded of fine bright dust in winter than in summer. This phenomenon possibly explains the seasonal contrast changes. Some scientists still believe, however, in the appealing idea that Martian dark areas darken in spring and summer because of the growth and proliferation of a dense cover of Martian vegetation. And, the reasoning goes, if there are plants, why not animals?

To discover whether the Martian environment could actually support living organisms of the sort found on earth, a number of scientists have simulated the planet's conditions in the laboratory and subjected both plants and animals to them. The results have been favorable. At NASA's Ames Research Center, for instance, Richard Young and his co-workers have found that certain bacteria can live and multiply in a daily freeze-thaw cycle of −150° F. to 70° F. In other experiments, scientists have housed turtles and other small animals in plastic-domed "Mars jars" under conditions approaching low Martian pressure and lack of oxygen, and found that they survive. Some microorganisms, indeed, have survived a com-

A diagram of the trajectory of
Mariner 4 from earth to Mars in
1965 reveals the solutions to some
complex engineering problems. To
generate enough velocity to reach
the Martian orbit, which is farther from the sun than that of
earth, the craft had to be launched
in the same direction as earth's
revolution around the sun and rotation about its axis. Months later, Mariner crossed Mars' orbit,
performed observations, then
passed behind the planet into a
perpetual journey around the sun.

bined jolt of ultraviolet light, thin atmosphere, carbon dioxide, and low water content. Moreover, with an increase of water content—such as might be expected in microenvironments during the Martian spring—some earth soil microorganisms actually multiply and thrive.

Other scientists are designing instruments to be landed on Mars' surface, where they will search for life, automatically. A typical device will send out a grapple or an arm or a sticky string to gather samples of Martian surface material; it will then retrieve this material and examine it, either by testing for metabolic activity or with a microscope. It is possible that Mars only supports microorganisms, but even if there are larger forms of life there still must be microorganisms, so the designers have deliberately concentrated on detecting the smallest forms of life.

The design of such instruments is not easy. Various assumptions about the nature of life on Mars have to be built into every Martian life detector. For example, a device to examine metabolic activity must assume that Martian organisms will like the food that we send along, or that they will give off some particular gas such as carbon dioxide in a process of photosynthesis similar to that on earth. It is conceivable that Martian organisms could be so different from terrestrial ones that all the early instruments would give negative results even though the planet teemed with life. But we have to look for the type of life we know first.

For this detection to succeed, however, the greatest care must be taken not to contaminate the planet with terrestrial microorganisms. For this reason both the United States and the Soviet Union have publicly committed themselves to sterilizing all vehicles intended for landing on Mars—or on any other planet.

In the next decades we shall be sending our instruments to Mars, and they are sure to yield us much exciting new information. A thorough reconnaissance will obviously be followed by the landing of automatic devices—but there is a debate as to whether man himself ought to plan to attempt a landing on Mars because of the contamination problem. It can only be resolved after detailed unmanned studies of this intriguing planet.

Mercury, the closest planet to the sun, is also the smallest and swiftest of the nine planets. In diameter it is only half again as big as the earth's moon, and it whirls around the sun at a speed of thirty miles per second. When nearest to the sun, a distance of some twenty-eight million miles, Mercury receives more than ten times as much radiation as the earth and the moon. The maximum temperature has been measured at Mount Wilson and Mount Palomar as about 800° F. At its farthest distance from the sun, some forty-three million miles, Mercury is still hot enough (545° F.) to melt tin and lead. Fred Whipple has suggested that Mercury, rather than Pluto, should have been named for the god of the underworld.

Little is known about the planet Mercury, not only because of its small size, but because its nearness to the sun makes it hard to study. However, recent radar studies have brought us new knowledge of the planet and upset one important, long-standing assumption. Until a few years ago, astronomers firmly believed that Mercury spins on its axis once a year, always turning the same face to the sun as the moon does to the earth. Put another way, its rotation period was thought to be synchronous with its orbital period, both being 88 earth days. Astronomers' maps of the surface of Mercury seemed to confirm this hypothesis, and there were theoretical reasons for believing that the planet, so close to the sun, would be "locked" to it as the moon is to the earth.

In line with this belief, one side of Mercury was thought to be blazing hot, and the other side perpetually cold—in fact, not too far from absolute zero. But in 1964, radio astronomers using a 250-foot dish antenna in Australia found the temperature on the dark side to be about 62° F. Perhaps, it was thought, heat moves from the bright side of the planet to the dark side by conduction through the planet or by convective air currents. Neither explanation was convincing. Conduction through the planet would be a slow and inefficient process, and as for convection, the atmosphere seemed much too thin to be capable of conveying the amount of heat needed to warm up the dark side.

The puzzle of the warm temperature on the dark side was solved in 1965 when Gordon Pettengill and Rolf B. Dyce, using the powerful radio telescope at Arecibo, found that the earlier supposition of the rotation period of Mercury was wrong—that in fact it was 59 days (plus or minus five), almost exactly two thirds of its orbital period of 88 days. Thus all parts of the planet receive sunlight, though Mercury's night is quite long—about 176 earth days.

This startling discovery prompted other astronomers to recheck the drawings that had been made of the surface of Mercury during the previous forty years. They found that three other values for the rotation period would explain the features observed just as well as the 88-day period, and one of them was the 59-day period observed by Pettengill and Dyce.

This illustrates a point about the limitations of scientific evidence. The early drawings of Mercury were consistent with an 88-day period, but that is not the same thing as *proving* an 88-day period. It has been shown time and again that a scientific theory which satisfactorily explains all the information known about a subject may have to be completely revised on the finding of one new fact.

From what little is known about Mercury, the planet presents a stark picture, somewhat like the moon in pitted, desolate appearance. Only on the dark side would temperatures be bearable. If there is an atmosphere at all, it probably would not contain oxygen, a gas too light to be held by the small planet with its weak gravitational pull. If a visitor beheld the sun, it would look enormous, and he would be risking lethal radiation. Astronomers agree that Mercury would be one of the last places to look for signs of life. Because of its lack of atmosphere, however, the planet should be much easier to explore than the shrouded and mysterious Venus, and because of its closeness to the sun, Mercury may be an ideal site for an instrumented research station, which could study our nearest star.

The innermost planet, Mercury,
is so close to the sun that it
is extremely difficult to observe.
By day it is obscured by the
sun's dazzling light and at night
it is visible only for brief
moments just above the horizon.
Its shadow can be discerned, however, while in transit across the
sun's face, as in the photograph
below, where an arrow indicates the
tiny planet. (The line across the
sun is produced by the camera
shutter; the other discolorations
are a prominent group of sunspots.)

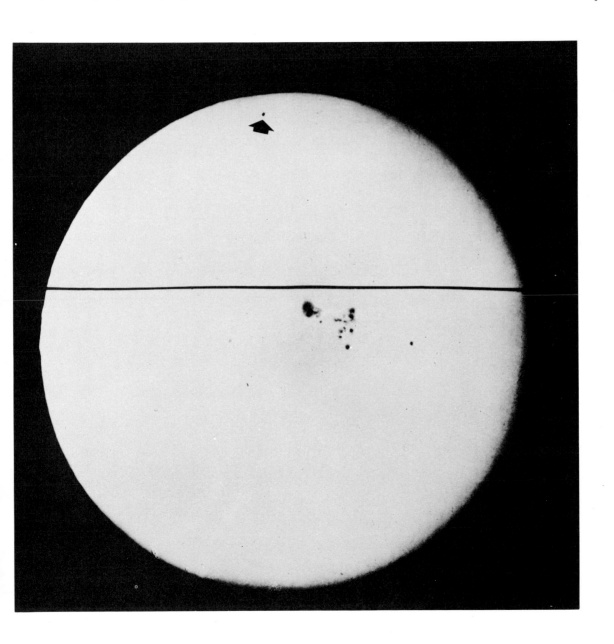

# 7. THE JOVIAN PLANETS AND BEYOND

A spaceship leaving Mars would have to cross a great gulf of space—more than four times the earth-sun distance—to reach Jupiter, the next major planet outward from the sun and the largest of a very different planetary group, of which Saturn, Uranus, and Neptune are the other members. These are known as the Jovian planets—giant worlds shrouded in heavy atmospheres that whirl about their axes faster than any of the terrestrial planets.

Of the four Jovians, Jupiter, the most impressive, is appropriately named for the king of the gods. It is thirteen hundred times larger than the earth in volume; two and a half times the mass of all the other planets combined; and attended by twelve satellites, more than any other planet. Escape velocity from Jupiter's surface is estimated at 130,000 miles per hour, compared with a mere 25,000 to get free from the earth.

Through the telescope Jupiter shows up as a flattened disk, somewhat like a squashed volley ball, with dark belts that parallel the planet's equator. These belts are separated by yellowish bands, or zones. Both belts and zones change color. By focusing on a patch of color an observer can follow its motion and determine the rate of rotation of the atmosphere (we can only guess at the rate of rotation of the planet itself). Jupiter's atmosphere, like that of the gaseous sun, actually rotates faster at the equator than it does at the poles; the cloud layers make one complete revolution every 9 hours and 55 minutes at typical temperate zone latitudes, as compared with 9 hours and 50 minutes at the equator. Excluding the asteroids, Jupiter is the fastest spinning planet in the solar system. In contrast, however, it takes its time revolving around the sun—nearly twelve years to cover the three billion miles of its orbital path. The inclination of Jupiter's equator to its orbit is so small that there are no seasons on the planet.

Jupiter's moons move in such a peculiar fashion that they would confuse anyone trying to figure out a usable calendar from their movements. The four tiny outermost moons swing through their orbits as far out as 10,000,000 miles from the planet, while the closest of the inner moons is no farther than 112,000 miles away, about half the distance of our own moon from earth. The outermost moons revolve around Jupiter in a retrograde direction, that is, in paths opposite that of the planet's rotation and opposite the inner moons' orbits.

The more orderly inner satellites include the four brightest and largest of Jupiter's moons, which have been known since Galileo's day. Though called the Galilean satellites, they were actually named by Simon Marius, a contemporary of Galileo, as Io, Europa, Ganymede, and Callisto—after consorts and attendants of Jupiter in classical mythology. Thereafter, each of the moons discovered was designated by a Roman numeral, V through XII.

One of the earliest ideas about Jupiter's composition, suggested in the 1930's by astronomer Rupert Wildt, was that the planet probably contained great amounts of hydrogen and helium. These are gases light enough to account for its over-all low density, which is about one fourth that of the earth; they are also the most abundant atoms in the sun and stars. Wildt also proposed that (as in the primitive days on earth) hydrogen might have combined with nitrogen and carbon, which are also fairly abundant cosmically, to form ammonia ($NH_3$) and methane ($CH_4$). The presence of these gases might account for the dark absorption bands in the Jovian spectrum.

Picking up this thought, Theodore Dunham of the Mount Wilson Observatory introduced methane and ammonia separately into a long pipe, transmitted a light beam through them, and investigated the results with a spectroscope. He found that the spectral lines and bands in the laboratory specimens agreed in wavelength with the dark bands of the spectrum of Jupiter. In addition, the existence of these two gases implied that the Jovian atmosphere was filled with hydrogen, the original hydrogen, it is thought, from which the planet was formed. While earth and the other terrestrial planets lost much of their original complement of light gases because of their relatively weak gravity and high upper-atmospheric temperatures, the Jovian planets evidently retained their hydrogen and helium because of their strong gravity and lower temperature.

More recent spectroscopic observations have confirmed that hydrogen and helium comprise the bulk of Jupiter's atmosphere and that methane and ammonia are present in small amounts—around 0.1 per cent. The temperatures in and above the clouds of Jupiter, as measured spectroscopically and by determining the infrared radiation emitted by the planet,

are less than $-95°$ F. This is not cold enough to condense out hydrogen, helium, or methane, but ammonia probably will be condensed at such temperatures, and the visible clouds of Jupiter are believed to be made up of ammonia rather than of water vapor as on earth. If hydrogen has combined with carbon and with nitrogen on Jupiter to form methane and ammonia, it seems reasonable to expect that it has also combined with oxygen to form water, since oxygen is just as abundant cosmically as carbon and nitrogen. This would have to happen, however, at much greater depths than those into which we have penetrated as yet, where the temperatures are far too low for it to condense out. Astronomers think it quite likely that water condensation clouds exist in Jupiter's lower atmosphere, below the ammonia clouds, although the presence of water has never been detected directly.

Jupiter's atmosphere is very extensive and much deeper than that of the earth. We have no idea how far down the atmosphere extends before the surface is reached. We do not even know whether there *is* a surface on Jupiter in the ordinary sense. It is quite possible that the atmosphere becomes denser and denser with increasing depth, eventually becoming quite thick and gradually fading into what we would call a solid, without there even being the clear demarcation of a surface. Pressures in the planet's interior are so great that the hydrogen there may be formed into metallic hydrogen, a material unknown on earth.

Seen through a telescope, Jupiter is a brilliant, swirling mélange of browns, yellows, oranges, blues, and reds. Yet in ordinary visible light hydrogen, helium, methane, ammonia, and water are entirely colorless; some other molecule must be present in Jupiter's clouds. In 1955 Francis Owen Rice, a chemist at Catholic University, suggested that the coloring material might be chemical fragments known as free radicals. On earth free radicals are rare and short-lived because they are rapidly destroyed by collision with other molecules. But at the low temperatures and low densities that characterize Jupiter's upper atmosphere, some free radicals could exist—and some of these molecular fragments, composed of carbon, hydrogen, nitrogen, and oxygen atoms, are indeed brightly colored.

Harold Urey had a more dramatic idea. To him it seemed more likely that the colors were due to organic molecules that were produced by interactions of methane, ammonia, and hydrogen in the Jovian atmosphere. Carl Sagan and his colleagues tested this idea in the laboratory by simulating the atmosphere of Jupiter, supplying energy to the mixture of gases, and then investigating the results with a computer. They found that simple organic molecules were produced quite readily, along with some more complex ring-shaped organic molecules that were brightly colored. More recently, instrumented rockets have taken ultraviolet spectra of Jupiter that independently suggest that quite complex organic molecules exist both in and above the planet's clouds. This is not altogether surprising, since the Jovian atmosphere today is thought to be very similar to the primitive earthly atmosphere in which the organic molecules arose that may have been the precursors of life on earth, and Jupiter's atmospheric temperatures are not too extreme, in the lower reaches, to support the more complex organic molecules of life itself.

The Jovian atmosphere's most striking feature is a huge, apparently permanent oval shape known as the great Red Spot. Twenty-five thousand miles long and eight thousand miles wide, the spot lies in a bright band called the south tropical zone. Its color varies from brick red to pink to faint gray; in the 1880's the spot grew so pale that astronomers concluded it was disappearing. But the spot is still there, and so is its mystery.

Over the years, many theories have been put forward to explain the spot's existence. Jean Dominique Cassini, the seventeenth-century astronomer who was among the first to notice the spot, observed that its rate of rotation was irregular. If the spot were due to some surface feature (a high mountain, for example), then it should move with the planet, which would mean that the motion of the planet itself must be irregular—an idea that was difficult for early astronomers to accept. A concept that gained favor late in the nineteenth century was that the spot is a solid object floating in a bed of gases. The raft hypothesis, as it is called, would explain why the spot moves with irregular speed and why on the average it moves more slowly than the clouds that surround it.

But other things were harder to explain. How could a solid object stay afloat in the atmosphere instead of sinking to the planet's surface? And why hasn't the spot migrated toward the equator of the swiftly revolving planet, where the movement is greatest?

In 1961 Raymond Hide, a British geophysicist at the Massachusetts Institute of Technology, proposed a new hypothesis to explain the spot. According to Hide, a surface feature on Jupiter—either a rise or a depression—deflects the gases whirling over it and causes a shaft of relatively stagnant air, known as a Taylor column (after G. I. Taylor, the British fluid mechanist), to extend upward into the atmosphere. Hide believed that the spot represented the top of this column, not the surface feature itself, and its singularity was simply because other irregularities on the planet's surface were below the critical size at which a Taylor column would be created. As for the irregularity of the spot's rotation rate, Hide is prepared to believe—as are other present-day scientists—that the entire planet does indeed revolve with irregular speed. We know now that there are irregularities in the earth's spin also, though they are far more subtle than those of the giant planet.

Jupiter continues to surprise astronomers. Recently, Frank Low of the University of Arizona, using a germanium bolometer, an instrument highly sensitive to infrared radiation, determined that Jupiter actually gives off more energy than it receives from the sun. Jupiter is probably too cold a body to be generating heat from thermonuclear reactions in its interior, as stars do. More likely, the planet is undergoing a process of slow contraction, generating heat as its materials are squeezed toward the center, a process common in the early history of stars, before their interior temperatures are hot enough to initiate thermonuclear reactions.

Another recent Jovian surprise occurred when radio astronomers found that Jupiter was emitting radio waves of great intensity. Planets were originally regarded as unlikely sources of radio emission, but in 1955 Kenneth L. Franklin and Bernard F. Burke, using a radio telescope near Washington, D.C., noticed tremendous bursts of radio waves coming from Jupiter. The bursts, some as powerful as ten million kilowatts at their source, sometimes occurred in rapid succession, the product of "storms" lasting as long as two hours.

In addition to these rapid bursts of activity, astronomers discovered a continuous, unchanging emission at long radio wavelengths. For this to be coming from some hot region of the Jovian atmosphere would mean that temperatures there were in excess of 180,000° F., far too hot to be reasonable for the upper atmosphere. This represented a puzzle until 1959, when Frank Drake of Cornell suggested the alternative explanation that the emissions are caused not by planetary heat but by electrons being impelled at very high velocities by the planet's strong magnetic field—a Jovian analogue of the Van Allen radiation belt around the earth.

More recently, scientists at the California Institute of Technology, using a microwave interferometer, have confirmed that this continuous emission from Jupiter does indeed come from a gigantic radiation belt extending to a distance several times the planet's radius.

The shorter radio bursts are probably also connected with this belt, perhaps caused by the sporadic dumping into the atmosphere of charged particles that ordinarily would be trapped by the Jovian magnetic field.

For all its vast distance from the earth, Jupiter is the closest and most accessible of the Jovian planets. These are in a much earlier stage of evolution than are the terrestrial planets, and when, in a few years, we start to fly spacecraft toward Jupiter to investigate the mysteries of its atmosphere, we may be granted an unrivaled opportunity to realize what earth was like in its primordial state.

Half a billion miles of blackness separate Jupiter from Saturn, the second of the Jovian planets and by far the most striking. The two planets are similar in several ways: Saturn is only slightly smaller, its day is only half an hour longer, it has almost as many moons (ten), and its composition is probably very nearly identical. Saturn has bands of color parallel to its equator, like those of Jupiter, though they are not as distinct. But Saturn's density is only a fraction of Jupiter's—in fact, Saturn is so light it would float in water—and hence its gravitational pull is milder.

The most distinctive features of Saturn, of course, are the thin, flat rings that gird the planet at its equator. Ancient Babylonian and Egyptian astronomers knew of Saturn's existence and the Romans made the planet a symbol of the harvest, but identification of the rings had to await the invention of the telescope.

Even then, the rings of Saturn eluded discovery. Their rotational axis is tilted to Sat-

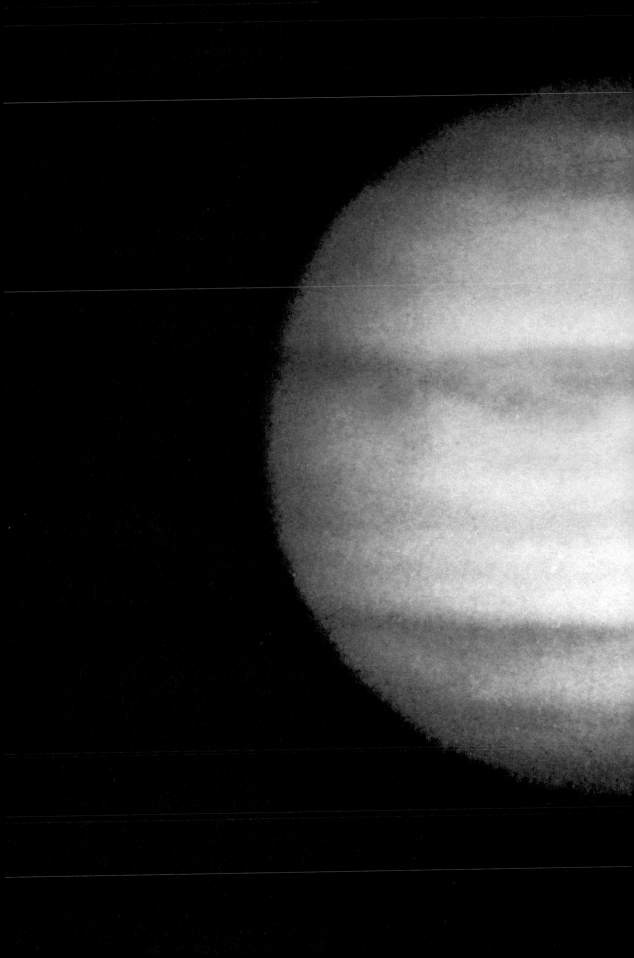

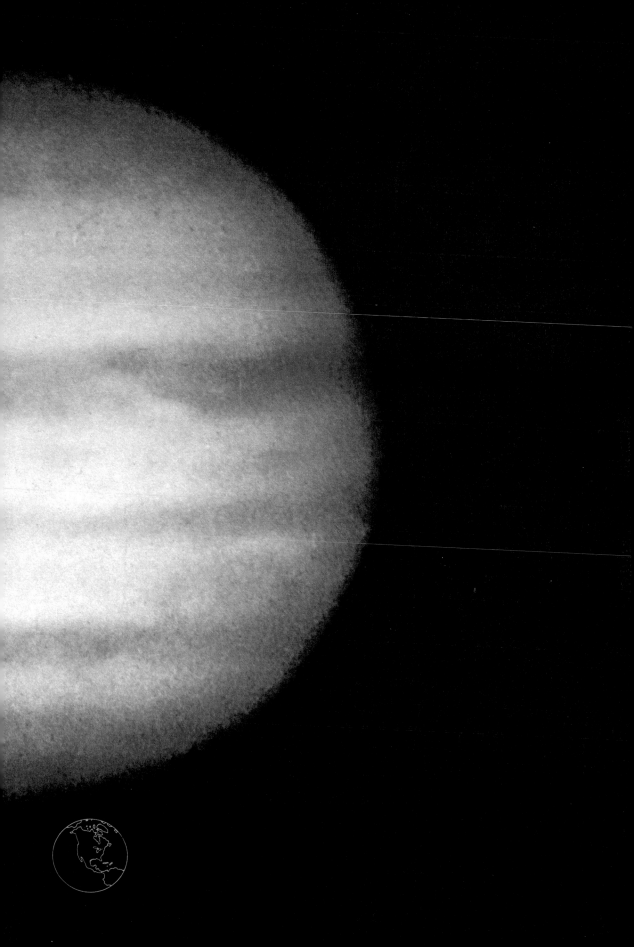

Saturn, with its dramatic girdle of rings, is one of the most beautiful members of the solar system; but for the crude telescopes of the 17th century, it was a most confusing object. Galileo guessed that it was some sort of triple planet. The Dutch physicist and astronomer Christian Huygens (left) perfected a new method of grinding and polishing lenses that made possible a telescope of clearer definition. In 1655 he announced his solution to the mystery: Saturn possessed circular rings. He also found that it had a moon. His contemporary, Jean

*Dominique Cassini (right), director of the recently opened Paris Observatory, soon discovered four more satellites and the division of the planet's ring that still bears his name. Cassini's original drawing (above), dated 1676, also indicates at least one of the planet's belts.*

urn's orbit, and there are periods during the planet's thirty-year trip around the sun when the rings, as seen from earth, are too thin to be observed when viewed edgewise. Galileo saw the rings approximately face-on in 1610, and drew ear-like appendages that he described as being "like two servants supporting an old gentleman." Two years later they seemed to be gone. Disputes about these elusive appendages went on for half a century, until the eminent Dutch scientist Christian Huygens established their existence and explained why they could not always be clearly seen.

Huygens actually thought Saturn had only one ring, but in 1675 Cassini detected a black line or gap that divided the ring into two rings. This gap is now known as Cassini's division. The third and innermost ring—dark and very faint and known as the crape ring—went undetected until 1850, when George Bond discovered it while observing Saturn through a telescope at Harvard.

From Huygens' time onward, the rings invited speculation about their origin and composition. Like most of his predecessors, William Herschel, the great eighteenth-century astronomer, thought the rings were solids, and for most of his life he believed that the Cassini division was not a true gap at all but a dark band in the continuous solid. In 1791 he abandoned this notion, having convinced himself that the blackness of the gap consistently matched that of the background sky.

The idea that the rings were solid remained alive until 1859, when James Clerk Maxwell proved that they could not be solid (or liquid

either, for that matter), but would have to be made up of billions of small particles. Only in that form, with each small particle constituting a kind of independent moon, could the rings be stable. Otherwise, the gravitational forces of nearby Saturn would tear the rings apart. In 1917, two British astronomers, Maurice Ainslie and John Knight, observed Saturn's outer ring passing in front of a distant star. The star did not disappear entirely, proving that the ring is translucent and suggesting that it is indeed made up of particles.

Spectroscopic studies have confirmed Maxwell's argument that the rings are made of small particles. If each particle is behaving like a separate moon, then the innermost particles will move much faster than the outermost, just as Mercury moves around the sun much faster than Pluto. By measuring the Doppler shift of spectral lines from the rings, scientists have been able to calculate their speeds of revolution and determine that the innermost particles move fastest. At the inner edge of the outer ring, particles complete an orbit of the planet more than two hours faster than particles at the outer edge.

Gerard Kuiper's spectrographic studies have led him to conclude that the particles in the rings, if not actually hoarfrost, are coated with ice. Until recently most astronomers believed the rings were at least ten miles thick, but from measurements of their brightness Allan Cook and Frederick Franklin of the S.A.O. have suggested that the rings are considerably thinner.

Despite these speculations, almost nothing is known with certainty about the rings, least

of all how they got there. Perhaps a moon of Saturn got too close to the planet and disintegrated. Perhaps the particles were there at Saturn's birth but for some reason failed to join in the condensation process that formed the planet. Whatever their origin, they are held in orbit around Saturn by a combination of centrifugal force and gravitational pull, and they are too close to the planet ever to congeal into a single moon. They are influenced by the innermost moons of Saturn, however, in a way that explains the positions of the gaps between the rings.

In 1867 Daniel Kirkwood, an American astronomer, pointed out that if a particle in Saturn's rings had an orbital period that was a simple fraction of the orbital period of one of the inner moons, a harmonic relationship would exist between particle and moon. Every few orbits of the particle it would be in the same relative position with the moon. The cumulative effect of the moon's gravitational tug on the particle would eventually so perturb the motion of the particle that it would oscillate right out of the region of the rings. Neighboring particles would respond in the same manner, thus creating a gap.

Kirkwood applied this theory to the Cassini division and to the gap dividing the main rings from the crape ring, and showed that if particles existed there, they would have orbital periods that are simple fractions—one half, one third, et cetera—of the orbital period of Saturn's inner moons. More recent work at S.A.O. by Fred Franklin suggests only one moon may be involved in this traffic control—Mimas.

Christian Huygens, discoverer of the rings, also discovered Titan, Saturn's largest moon. Titan is almost as large as the planet Mercury and is known to support an atmosphere. Huygens, it is said, stopped looking for other moons because his discovery in 1655 brought the number of bodies in the solar system to the mystical number 12. His contemporary, Cassini, soon upset this neat scheme by finding four more moons of Saturn, which he diplomatically proposed to name in honor of his patron, Louis XIV; but the proposal never caught on.

William Herschel, who discovered two more satellites of Saturn, was content to refer to all seven moons by number, but, early in the nineteenth century, his son John gave all the moons classical names. When George Bond, discoverer of Saturn's innermost ring, found an eighth moon in 1848, he followed the younger Herschel's lead by naming it Hyperion. So did William H. Pickering, who in 1898 discovered Saturn's ninth and outermost satellite, Phoebe.

Pickering thought he spotted a tenth moon, but other astronomers could not confirm his observations. As it happened, a tenth moon was waiting to be discovered, but not the one Pickering thought he saw. Audouin Dollfus found it in December, 1966, and named it Janus. That Janus eluded discovery for so long is understandable, for it is only three hundred miles in diameter and too close to the rings to be clearly distinguishable from them.

Saturn hides its surface beneath a thick, opaque atmosphere, very much like Jupiter's. Infrared and radio measurements indicate that Saturn's cloud temperatures are colder than

The rings of Saturn (below) are
made up of swarms of tiny particles
orbiting the planet in a ring-
shaped plane extending outward for
some 38,000 miles into space but,
incredibly, no more than a few
miles thick. The planet itself
has only a few bands, belts, and
spots, which probably means that
its atmosphere is less turbulent,
as well as colder, than that of
Jupiter. At left, a Bonestell
painting shows Saturn viewed at
a distance of 2,200,000 miles
from its seventh satellite, Iapetus.

*William Herschel (right), the organist who became 18th-century England's ablest astronomer, discovered Uranus in 1781 during a methodical search of the sky with a 6.2-inch reflector he had made himself. The four appendages and "ring" around the planet shown at far right are artifacts, caused by light diffraction around the struts supporting the secondary mirror of the 82-inch McDonald Observatory reflector that made the photograph. The dot inside the ring is Uranus' fifth moon, Ariel.*

those of the Jovian clouds, but it is probable that the temperature rises closer to the Saturnian surface, like the temperature in the earth's own atmosphere. Saturn, like Jupiter, emits more thermal energy than it receives from the sun, but there is no sign of a strong radio emission, and it is just possible that the planet's rings sweep up the charged particles that would otherwise constitute a Saturnian Van Allen belt.

Beyond Saturn lie the three planets that are too dim and too slow in their orbits to have been known to ancient and medieval astronomers. Two of them, Uranus and Neptune, are similar in several ways. Both are three to four times larger in diameter, though far less dense than the earth; Uranus, the bigger of the two, is only two thirds as dense as Neptune. Both appear greenish in the telescope, probably because of very strong absorption of red light by the methane that is known to be prominent in their atmospheres. Uranus, the closer of the two, takes eighty-four years to orbit the sun, while Neptune takes nearly twice as long.

Uranus has one unusual characteristic: it rotates at nearly a right-angle plane of its revolution about the sun, like a ball rolling across the floor, and if one takes the upward tilting pole of the planet to be its north pole, the spin turns out to be retrograde—an intriguing characteristic Uranus shares with Venus.

Uranus was discovered by William Herschel in 1781 after a systematic search of the sky with a superb telescope whose lenses he himself had ground. The discovery catapulted him to fame and he was soon able to give up the career

as an organist with which he had supported his astronomical research. So startling was the discovery of a new planet, the first in more than two thousand years, that scientists could not agree on how it should be named. Herschel wanted to call it Georgium Sidus, in honor of his king, George III, while other astronomers wanted to name it for Herschel himself. Eventually the classical precedents won out, and the planet was named after the god who was Saturn's father. Herschel also discovered two moons of Uranus, which he christened Oberon and Titania. Three other moons remained to be discovered, the most recent in 1948.

Almost from the moment of its discovery, Uranus gave astronomers trouble. They calculated its orbit with care, but the planet disobeyed their calculations; it was never where it was expected to be. Could another planet, farther out still, be tugging at it? John Couch Adams, a young Cambridge mathematician, thought so and in 1845 he showed by theoretical calculations where the planet ought to be located. None of Britain's senior astronomers, however, took Adams' calculations seriously.

In France, on the other hand, the renowned astronomer Urbain Jean Leverrier, also worked out the calculations, and on a September night in 1846, Johann G. Galle at the Berlin Observatory observed the new planet in the heavens just where Leverrier said it should be.

In subsequent years a dispute arose between French and English astronomers over who should be credited with the discovery of Neptune. (Adams himself kept out of it.) The English finally contented themselves by claiming

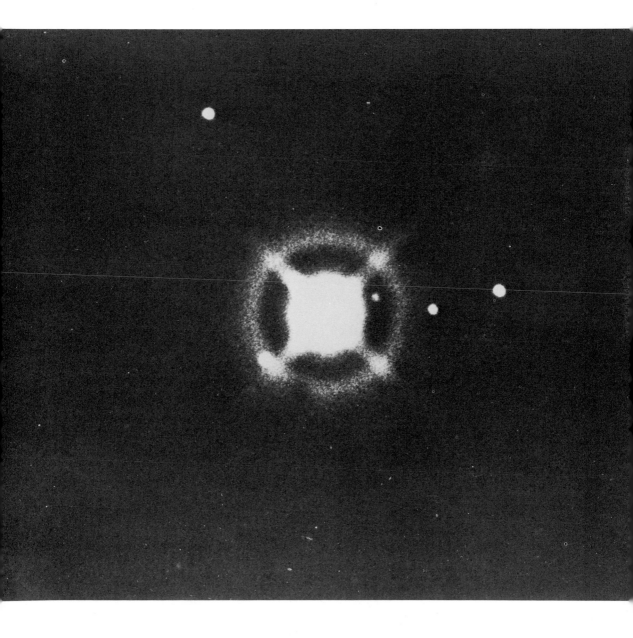

*Percival Lowell was so convinced of the presence of a ninth planet, somewhere beyond Neptune, that he organized a systematic search for it from his private observatory in Arizona. In 1930, Clyde Tombaugh (left), who was then a young assistant at Lowell Observatory, found the planet, Pluto (indicated by arrow at far left), by careful examination of photographic plates taken in the area of the star Delta Geminorum, which itself appears, greatly distorted, beside the tiny planet.*

credit for finding Neptune's large satellite, Triton, located by a Liverpool astronomer, William Lassell, a few weeks after the planet itself was first discovered. (A second satellite, Nereid, was found in 1949 by Gerard Kuiper.)

The presence of Neptune answered the problem of irregularities in the orbit of Uranus. Or did it? When scientists recalculated the orbit of Uranus, taking the disturbing effect of Neptune into consideration, the planet still refused to obey their calculations. Moreover, there were unaccountable perturbations in the orbit of Neptune itself. Could there be still another planet farther out from the sun?

One astronomer who thought so was Percival Lowell, popularizer of a Martian "civilization." He diligently worked out the calculations of where Planet X, as he called it, ought to be, but after he died in 1916, the search for the new planet went into abeyance. It was revived in 1929, when Clyde W. Tombaugh, an assistant at the Lowell Observatory, began systematically photographing the night sky, comparing plates of identical areas of the sky taken several nights apart, looking for an object that moved during the interval. After nearly a year of this painstaking work, Tombaugh found the elusive planet. (His firsthand account of the search is reproduced in the Appendix to this book.) As much in honor of Percival Lowell as of the god of the underworld, the new planet was named Pluto and given the symbol of an interlocked P and L, a combination of Lowell's initials.

Yet still a mystery remained. Pluto was expected to be a giant planet like its neighbors, to account for its effect on their orbits. Yet all evidence pointed to a tiny planet—perhaps only thirty-six hundred miles in diameter—that would have to have a fantastically high density to be responsible for the perturbations in the orbits of Uranus and Neptune. Could still another planet be responsible? For years Tombaugh kept up his systematic search for one, looking amid millions of stars for an object that moved, but he turned up nothing. And though a number of theories have been put forth to explain Pluto's extraordinary tug on its neighbors, the mystery is unsolved.

Pluto is so small, its orbit so highly elliptical, and its rotational period so slow (six and a half days), that some astronomers believe it may once have been a moon of Neptune that somehow, in a cataclysmic event, escaped Neptune's pull and became a planet in its own right. However, it has recently been shown that Pluto and Neptune are held by gravitational forces to a repeating orbital cycle of twenty thousand years; this precludes Pluto from going anywhere near Neptune, and makes the idea that Pluto is an escaped satellite less tenable.

Beyond Pluto lies the blackness that separates the sun and its known family of planets from the nearest stars, many light-years away. That space may be empty of planetary bodies which owe their parentage to the sun. Yet beyond the reaches of our solar system, astronomers generally agree, millions of planets must be circumnavigating other suns. None has yet been found, though there are a few hints; but that is because the new astronomy is young and we are entering a fresh era of discovery.

107

# Blazing-Stars
## Meſſengers of GOD's Wrath:
### In a few ſerious and ſolemn Meditations upon the wonderful

# COMET:

Which now appears in our Horizon, *April*, 1759: Together with a ſolemn Call to Sinners, and Counſel to Saints; how to behave themſelves when GOD is in this wiſe ſpeaking to them from Heaven.

---

CANST thou by ſearching find out *God*,
  The high and Holy one,
  Or the almighty Majeſty,
Unto Perfection.
Where waſt thou, ſaith th'eternal GOD,
  To *Job*, that holy Man,
When I the Earth's Foundations laid,
  Declare now if you can.
When th'Morning Stars together ſang,
  With glorious Melody,
And all the Sons of GOD did ſhout
  With loud triumphant Joy?
Where is the Place where Light doth dwell,
  And as for Darkneſs, where?
If thou doſt know its vaſt Receſs,
  My Servant now declare.
The lovely Pſalmiſt, when he'd ſpread
  The great JEHOVAH's Fame,
Declares,---He numbers all the Stars,
  And calls them all by Name.
That Fire, and Miſt, and Hail, and Snow,
  Whirlwinds with one Accord,
Obey the holy juſt Command
  Of their moſt glorious Lord.
And in the Time of *Iſrael's* Straights,
  That awful Day,
The Stars in martial Order fought,
  'Gainſt wicked *Siſera*.
Theſe are among the wond'rous Works
  Of the eternal ONE,
Who also chearfully obey,
  When he ſpeaks, lo! 'tis done,
He bids them ſtand o'er Kingdoms, Towns,
  All in a flaming Fire;
And great Attention to his Voice,
  The Lord doth now require.
The ancient Fathers learn'd and wiſe,
  When they did ſee them burn,
Prognoſticated evil Things,
  Soon on the World would come.
Heralds of GOD his Meſſengers,
  The World to preach unto,
And learn'd and wiſe and holy Men
  Fully agree thereto.
O what amazing Changes, have
  A ſinful World oft ſeen?
And Nations, Kingdoms, Cities too
  Where theſe great Sights have been.
Great Griefs and ſore Calamities,
  Have oft ſucceeded them,
And ſore Deſtruction overtook
  A World of ſinful Men,
But to relate, one, two, or three,
  At this time may ſuffice,
Together with the one you ſee
  Now blazing in your Eyes.
When this our World was young in Years
  Not ſeventeen Hundred quite,
A large and blazing Comet was
  Preſented in their Sight.
Soon after which *Methuſelah*
  The oldeſt Man on Earth,
Surrendred up his Life into
  The Hands of potent Death.
And lo! the Year, the very Year
  After that he was dead,
The old World all, except eight Souls,
  By Water periſhed.

An hundred Inſtances or more
  I might have added here,
But by two faithful Witneſſes
  Great Truths eſtabliſh'd are.
In ſixteen hundred ſixty four
  Behold in lofty Sky,
A flaming Comet did appear
  Large and conſpicuouſly.
Soon after which moſt awful Sight
  A bloody War began
'Twixt *England* and the *Hollanders*
  Moſt violent did become.
An awful Plague in *England* too
  As ever had been known,
Near Seven Thouſand in one Week,
  Unto the Pit went down.
That in the Space of but one Year,
  An hundred thouſand fell,
Victims unto voracious Death,
  An awful Spectacle.
Soon after which, even the next Year,
  The *Papiſts* do conſpire,
And by their Craft and Subtilty,
  LONDON they ſet on Fire.
Behold vaſt Clouds of Smoke aſcend,
  As in the Cloud,
By means whereof the Moon was dark
  And Sun became like Blood.
In ſixteen Hundred ſixty five
  In our Hemiſphere,
A burning blazing Comet did
  For many Nights appear.
Which follow'd was with ſcorching Drought
  In *Britain*, and this Land,
And might have ſoon deſtroy'd us all,
  Hadn't GOD witheld his Hand.
Thus we were ſpar'd; but O behold,
  What awful Trouble fell,
On many Places in the World
  No Tongue can fully tell.
To name but one or two dear Soul's
  Or more if you require,
In *Hungary* four hundred Towns
  Deſtroy'd by Sword and Fire.
Great Floods o'erflow'd the *Netherlands*,
  That in one fatal Night,
Thouſands, ye Thouſands there were drown'd
  Before the Morning Light.
But to return, wiſe holy Men
  They verily have Thought
That thoſe great flaming Meſſengers,
  Where never ſent for nought.
No, no, Dear Soul's they don't think ſo
  But rather that they are,
The Signs of GOD's moſt dreadful Wrath
  And ſad Events declare:
As awful, dreadful, bloody Wars,
  Plagues, Peſtilence and Storms,
'Mongſt Nations great, and mighty they
  Portend awful Alarms.
That they are Meſſengers of Death,
  Sent by the mighty GOD,
And therefore he that ſees and views,
  Should bow before the LORD.
Floods they may cauſe, and Droughts likewiſe
  And Earthquakes ſtrong and great,
So that the Earth's Foundations,
  May tremble, ſhake, and quake,

A fam'd Philoſopher of old,
  Conjectur'd that before
The mighty GOD to Judgment comes
  In his majeſtick Power;
Comets and fearful Sights more brief
  Then ever yet have been,
More frequently and commonly
  Would in the World be ſeen;
And are not we now Witneſſes,
  Let all our Fathers ſay,
If ever GOD before them paſt
  In ſuch an awful Way.

### IMPROVEMENT.

AND now O Earth, O Earth attend
  The mighty Voice of GOD,
Who in his Wrath is coming down
  By Sickneſs; Fire and Sword.
GOD calls aloud, awake, awake,
  And from your Slumber riſe,
When in the Heavens he ſets ſuch Sign
  Of Wonder and Surprize.
Adore the mighty ſovereign LORD
  And bow before him low,
Who ſends his timely Warnings forth
  Before he ſtrikes the Blow.
Prepare, O Land, prepare for what
  The LORD's about to do,
For what awful Events are nigh
  The LORD alone doth know.
Unto your Chambers enter ſtrait
  GOD's Folk, and ſhut the Door,
Till all the Storms of his fierce Wrath
  Shall all be paſt and o'er.
And O you chriſtleſs graceleſs Souls,
  Can you abide GOD's Power?
When out of *Zion* he will ſhout
  And as a Lion roar.
When all his Wrath ſet in array
  Againſt your Souls will blaze,
O tell me Sinner, tell me where
  You'l find a ſecure Place.
If Death o'ertakes you in your Sins
  Then down to Hell you muſt,
And with the Priſoners there in Chains
  Eternally be curs'd.
And lo the Guilt of your Soul's Blood
  On your own Head will lie,
And ſo ſolorn and helpleſs be
  To all Eternity.
But O dear Sirs, there yet is Hope,
  Cry mightily to GOD,
To turn away his dreadful Wrath,
  And his devouring Sword.
*Zion's* Son's and Daughters now return
  Return unto the Lord,
Or elſe prepare to meet him ſoon
  With flaming Fire and Sword.
Caſt off your fooliſh vain Attire,
  With Sackcloth now be clad,
Which at this Day becomes a Land
  Who have provok'd their GOD.
Awake ye Prieſts of GOD the LORD,
  'Twixt Porch and Altar cry,
Spare, ſpare thy People bleſſed GOD,
  Let not *New-England* die.
Add Prayer and Faſting hereunto
  It may be GOD will hear,
And out of *Zion* ſend us Help
  And yet his People ſpare.

---

*BOSTON*: Printed and ſold by *R. Draper* in *Newbury-Street*; and by *Fowle & Draper* in *Marlborough-Street*. 1759.

# 8. COMETS, METEORS, AND ASTEROIDS

At six o'clock on the morning of June 30, 1908, passengers who were awake on the Trans-Siberian express peered out the windows to see a giant fireball, as big and bright as the sun, streaking across the sky. Moments after the object disappeared over the northern horizon, the train was rocked by the percussion of a deafening explosion. The engineer, thinking the train itself had exploded, grabbed the brake and brought the train to a jolting halt. But the explosion had occurred about three hundred miles away, and the shock wave it created was recorded on instruments as far away as England.

Nomads tending their reindeer near the site of the explosion watched in fright as their flimsy huts were blown to pieces. The reindeer fled in panic, and hundreds of them were trampled to death in the stampede. Miraculously, no human lives were lost, but forty miles from the explosion a man was knocked unconscious, factory windows were shattered, and doors were ripped from their hinges. Trees as far as twenty-five miles from the explosion snapped in half, and whole forests lay flattened with the tops of trees pointed away from the center of the blast.

As awesome and mysterious as the explosion was, no scientist went to investigate the site of the Great Tunguska Catastrophe, as it came to be called. Central Siberia was a long and uncomfortable journey from the major Russian halls of learning, and in the stormy, dying years of tsarist Russia, scientific expeditions took second place to other matters. Not until 1927, in fact, did a Soviet expedition reach the assumed

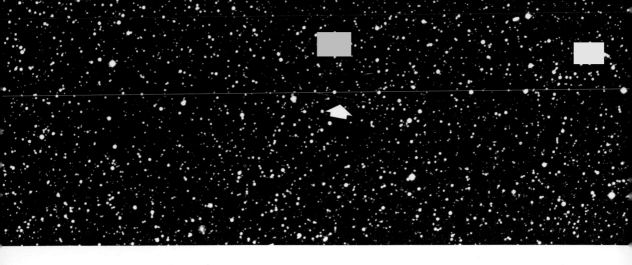

site of the explosion. That expedition, and every one since then, failed to clear up the mystery. No major impact crater has ever been found (though smaller craters have been seen), nor has any material turned up that can indisputably be linked with the explosion.

Scientists estimate that the Siberian blast released energy equivalent to twenty-five million tons of TNT exploded at an altitude of three miles. Explanations for the strange event abound: a meteorite, a comet, a chemical explosion, even a nuclear blast from an interstellar spaceship—and the recent suggestion that the explosion was caused by a piece of "antimatter" from another part of space.

Antimatter, as its name suggests, is a substance composed in an opposite fashion to matter as we know it. In atoms of ordinary matter the nuclei have positive charges and the surrounding electrons have negative charges; in antimatter it is the other way around. When antimatter comes into contact with ordinary matter, the oppositely charged particles annihilate each other and are totally converted into energy in the form of gamma rays. Some antimatter has been made experimentally by nuclear physicists, and has been observed for the brief period before it was annihilated by interaction with ordinary matter—of which the earth is entirely composed. Cosmologists have postulated that there is no apparent reason why matter should be preferred over antimatter and that there may be other regions of the universe in which antimatter is dominant and matter very rare. If a piece of antimatter from outer space entered our atmosphere, there is

no doubt that it would rapidly be annihilated in a fierce explosion, but in its details the hypothesis that the Tunguska explosion was caused by the impact of an antimatter meteorite does not hold up.

A more likely explanation is that the explosion resulted from an ordinary meteorite or comet impacting at such high velocity that no remnants of the impacting matter could easily be found afterward. If this is the case, it is an interesting reminder that while the bodies of the solar system move in stately serenity in their orbits, over a long enough period some of those orbits intersect and objects may collide. Such events are sufficiently rare to pose no immediate danger for the earth, but the crater-pocked surfaces of the moon and Mars are clear reminders that these violent impacts do occur.

The area of interplanetary space where collisions most frequently occur is the so-called asteroid belt, the region between Mars and Jupiter where countless thousands of the small planetary bodies known as asteroids orbit the sun and from time to time collide with one another as they do so. Most asteroids keep fairly strictly to this belt but several are nonconformists with extremely elliptical orbits. Some asteroids travel along planes that are at highly inclined angles to the planes of the planets themselves. Others cross the orbits of neighboring planets: Icarus actually gets closer to the sun than Mercury, and Hidalgo swings out almost to the orbit of Saturn. Several asteroids, crossing the orbit of the earth, have aroused fears of collision with our own planet.

In the summer of 1968, as Icarus—an irreg-

*Like the planets, the minor mem-*
*bers of our solar system orbit*
*the sun. Most of the rocky,*
*metallic asteroids keep to a belt*
*between the orbits of Mars and*
*Jupiter, though Icarus (arrowed*
*at left) swings close enough to*
*earth to have caused alarm.*
*The comets—aggregations of*
*frozen gases—mostly reside far*
*beyond the orbit of Pluto. Their*
*distinctive tails, like that of*
*the comet Humason below, are the*
*result of bombardment by charged*
*particles in the solar wind.*

ularly shaped asteroid about a mile in diameter —approached the earth, anxious callers telephoned observatories and planetariums all over the world. A group of San Francisco hippies, convinced of a collision that would set up tidal waves and inundate their city, sought refuge in the Colorado Rockies. As it happened, Icarus reached its closest point to earth on June 14— a comfortable four million miles away, exactly as had been calculated by many astronomers, including Brian Marsden of the S.A.O. By contrast, in 1937 the asteroid Hermes approached within half a million miles of the earth, a distance barely twice that from earth to moon, without any perceptible effect on the earth.

If the knowledge is any comfort, statistics show that the earth will be hit by an asteroid of appreciable size less than once every hundred thousand years. The great Meteor Crater in Arizona, four thousand feet in diameter, may be the result of such a collision. By one estimate, this crater is only five thousand years old, and the awesome spectacle of the collision may have been witnessed by local Indians. A longer established meteor crater is the Ries Basin—a bowl fifteen miles in diameter that surrounds the town of Nördlingen in Germany.

Asteroids as celestial bodies were unknown to man until 1801, when Giuseppi Piazzi, an Italian priest and astronomer, detected one through his telescope during the night after New Year's Day. The man who especially shared Piazzi's joy at the discovery was a German astronomer, Johann Elert Bode. Bode had popularized a simple formula predicting the distance from the sun of each of the planets, including the then recently discovered Uranus. This formula, which became known as Bode's law, called for a planet in the middle of the great gulf between Mars and Jupiter. A search for this planet was set in motion, and it ended with Piazzi's discovery of a small planetary body at the right distance.

In fact, Bode's law is not a law; neither is it Bode's. The formula had been worked out originally some years before by another German astronomer, J. D. Titius; by publicizing it, however, Bode got credit for it. The formula assigns the value 0 to Mercury, 3 to Venus, then 6, 12, and further doublings to the other planets in succession. Add 4 to each of these numbers, divide by 10, and the results are average distances expressed in astronomical units, that is, the earth-sun distance. (Neptune and Pluto, discovered many years later, do not conform to Bode's law, which in fact makes so many arbitrary assumptions that it is easier to memorize the planets' respective distances from the sun than to memorize the law itself.)

The body that Piazzi discovered was too small to be deserving of the name planet, and so was called an asteroid, meaning star-like, though the term planetoid is preferred for obvious reasons by some astronomers. Because the asteroid was small, Piazzi gave his discovery a feminine name, Ceres, and when three other asteroids were discovered in the first decade of the nineteenth century, they too were named for goddesses: Pallas, one of the many Greek names for Athena; Juno; and Vesta. Since then, more than sixteen hundred asteroids have been discovered and plotted, many

AEROLITES, METEORS &c.

more than classical mythology could provide names for. At least forty thousand smaller asteroids still await identification.

The discovery that the asteroids are concentrated in a belt between the orbits of Mars and Jupiter naturally led astronomers to speculate that once there had been a larger planet there, which exploded to form a number of minor planets and planetary fragments. It seems more likely that the material from which the solar system formed was prevented, in the region of the asteroid belt, from condensing into a planet because of the gravitational influence of the massive planet Jupiter nearby.

Observations of the light reflected from many asteroids indicate that they are probably not perfect spheres but are irregularly shaped. The spherical forms of the earth and the other planets are maintained by gravitational forces that are large enough to crush any major irregularities existing in them into this typical shape. The asteroids, however, are small enough to support their original irregularities, and to this extent they preserve a more accurate record of their early history than do the larger planets.

For this reason alone it would be fascinating to be able to look at an asteroid close up. But up to now this has been possible only remotely. Collisions among asteroids constantly chip off small pieces, some of which accidentally intercept the earth's orbit, fall into our atmosphere, and survive to land on the surface. When found they are known as meteorites.

Altogether about seven hundred meteorites have been observed in falling and have subsequently been recovered; some seventeen hundred more have been found on the ground after unobserved falls. An untold number of meteorites fall into the ocean, unseen and unrecovered. Harrison Brown of the California Institute of Technology estimates that some five hundred meteorites fall to the earth each year, of which only about seven are recovered for scientific investigation.

By their composition, meteorites generally comprise three categories: the stony meteorites, which are similar to the silicate rocks of the earth's mantle; the iron meteorites, which are heavy in iron and nickel and probably resemble the material deep in the earth's core; and the stony irons, which are intermediate in composition and constitute less than 5 per cent of the meteorites that have been found.

One of the largest stony meteorites ever dug up landed in Kansas in 1948 and weighed slightly more than a ton. The largest iron meteorite still lying at its point of impact, in South Africa, weighs about sixty tons, though fragments nearby would add another twenty tons to its original weight at the time of impact.

One particularly intriguing variety of stony meteorite is known as a carbonaceous chondrite —chondrite because it contains small glassy inclusions, called chondrules, that have cooled from a molten state early in the solar system's history; and carbonaceous because it contains up to 1 per cent of matter rich in carbon. This carbonaceous material consists of many of the same organic molecules that are found in living things on earth. Though some could be the result of "contamination" on earth, most of them are indigenous to the meteorite—arising on

Meteorites are objects larger
than meteors that survive their
journey into earth's atmosphere to
land on its surface. Occasional
giant specimens are discovered,
such as the Ahnighito iron meteorite below, which weighs more than
34 tons. It was found in Green-
land, where tradition held that
it had fallen from the sky; the
local Eskimos were using it as a
handy source of iron for their
knives and fish hooks. Even larger
meteorites, colliding with the
earth at high speeds, produce
craters as they do on the moon and
Mars. The great Meteor Crater (far
right) in Arizona, which is 4,000
feet across, may well have been
caused by a fragment of an asteroid, impacting with such energy that
it was completely vaporized. Meteorites are the only samples of
extraterrestrial material available in any quantity for our
study. To chemists and mineralo-
gists, investigation of meteorites'
interiors, such as that shown
in the microphotograph at right,
has revealed that these objects date
from the dawn of our solar system.

its parent body, probably located somewhere in the asteroid belt. Chemists have debated whether the organic matter in the carbonaceous chondrite need necessarily be produced by life, or whether it might be of the same sort of prebiological organic matter that gave rise to life on earth. In either case, the finding is of great significance.

Meteorites, as samples of extraterrestrial matter that has not been altered and weathered like the matter on earth's surface, offer almost the only current clues we have to the chemistry of the early history of the solar system. In an effort to acquire more of them for laboratory study, particularly the rare carbonaceous chondrites, a system of sixteen automatic camera stations in the midwestern United States, operated by the S.A.O. and known as the Prairie Network, constantly scrutinizes the heavens, recording the entry of meteorites and aiding in their recovery.

Meteors or shooting stars, as they are often called, are not to be confused with these meteorites. Meteors are not stars at all, in fact, but tiny particles, often no bigger than a grain of sand, which become incandescent on their high-speed entry into the earth's atmosphere, and are vaporized by frictional heating before they can penetrate much deeper than some sixty miles above the earth's surface. Meteors occur more often in some seasons of the year than in others, and when many of them are visible, the event is described as a meteor shower. These showers often occur when the earth passes through the remains of an extinct comet, and some meteors may well be cometary debris.

While the abundant tiny meteors burn up on entrance into the earth's atmosphere, the larger meteorites survive their journey, although their outer surfaces are heated often to melting point during their entry. In this respect the surface acts as a kind of heat shield, similar to the heat shield of manned space vehicles, that prevents the meteorite from burning up from friction as it enters the earth's atmosphere. Evidence of this is that a meteorite shortly after landing is often hot on the outside, though still intensely cold on the inside.

Objects even tinier than meteors also enter the earth's atmosphere in great numbers; these are so small that the atmosphere slows them down before they are heated to incandescence, and they then float gently down like a fine rain toward the surface of the planet. According to an estimate made by Fred Whipple, this fine dust adds between one and two million tons to the earth's mass every year.

It has taken a long time for man to understand the origins and composition of the mysterious smaller objects in space, but through history they have inspired him with a mixture of fear, superstition, and religious awe. Strange stones that apparently fell from the sky were believed to have magical properties, and at Mecca, the center of Moslem worship, a black stone that is probably a meteorite has been venerated for centuries. The glittering, evanescent meteor showers were also thought to be miraculous, and in some way connected with lightning. But by far the most spectacular and terrifying of the interplanetary objects have always been the comets with their hugely elongated tails that appear at intervals to transform man's vision of the heavens.

Until the seventeenth century, the advent of a comet was taken as a sure sign of God's wrath and calamities to come. It was not until Edmund Halley positively identified the comet of 1682 (that now bears his name) as the same comet that had previously terrified the world in 1607, 1531, and 1456, and predicted that it would return in the year 1758, that men began to realize that comets followed definite, but highly eccentric, orbital paths around the sun, and could be classed as celestial bodies rather than as signs of divine anger.

This did not prevent astrologers from continuing to believe that the years when comets appeared were specially significant. One minister, influenced by Halley's ideas on cometary activity, but considerably more credulous, managed to trace appearances of another comet at 574-year intervals back to the Flood— which he believed the comet had caused by some kind of magnetic attraction. Halley's comet itself, however, has appeared in the skies on several occasions that were historically memorable: in 451 Attila the Hun invaded Gaul with his armies, en route to Rome; in 1066 William the Conqueror overran England; in 1456 the Turks had taken Constantinople and were on the march into Europe—a threat so terrifying that the pope ordered prayers and supplications said in every Christian church.

The comet was due again in 1835 and this time a new kind of scare arose—that it might collide with the earth. But this panic was stilled, chiefly by better scientific understanding of the nature and behavior of comets, and Halley's comet came and went without any dire occurrences.

According to the Dutch astrophysicist Jan H. Oort, whose hypothesis is widely accepted, most of the comets—perhaps two hundred billion of them—reside in a belt beyond Pluto's orbit, extending halfway to the nearest star. Not all of them stay neatly in this outermost realm of the solar system; an estimated five million comets have orbits that bring them closer to the sun than Neptune.

The suggestion has been made that over the ages perturbations from stars have slightly altered the orbits of some comets, pushing them inward on a path toward the sun. Thus swayed, such a comet becomes what is known as a long-period comet, approaching the sun only once in several hundred years, sometimes only once in a million years. Others, by an accident of their trajectory, may fall under the influence of Jupiter's powerful gravitational field and assume orbits that never take them far from the sun again. These short-period comets complete their orbits as frequently as once every three and one-third years. All comets, however, move at very slow velocities.

The comets are the wild men of the solar system; not only do their orbital paths range widely in size and shape, but they are also subject to constant and unpredictable change as they are buffeted by the gravitational pull and radiation of the sun and the planets they pass. About half of the long-period comets move in retrograde orbits, that is, in a direction opposite to that of the planets. A few, some astronomers think, are drawn so close to the sun that they are sent off again in a new direction that carries them out past Pluto again, out past the tug of the solar system altogether.

While orbiting in the belt beyond Pluto, a comet would be an extremely cold object with a temperature close to absolute zero. Scientists are not certain whether comets have a core of solid, earth-like materials, but many agree with Fred Whipple's theory that the outer layers of the core, at least, consist of frozen methane, ammonia, and water, mixed with stony particles, somewhat like dirty snow. When a comet leaves its far-off home and ventures closer to the sun the snows begin to vaporize, forming a gaseous, misty layer known as a coma. As the comet moves nearer the sun and the process of disintegration speeds up, it expands in size. It also grows brighter, partly as a result of reflected sunlight, but also because radiation from the sun excites the molecules in the coma and causes them to fluoresce.

When a comet is within a distance from the sun about twice that of the earth's, it may begin to show a bright tail. Though called a tail, this always points away from the sun because it is not a wake but the result of the solar wind pushing against the comet. Some comets have heads that are 1,000,000 miles in diameter (though the average is about 100,000 miles). Sometimes a brilliant burst of light flashes from one of them, caused by the sudden release of gases that were trapped in solid particles. The tails can grow even more impressively than the heads; the longest measured to date is 200,000,000 miles.

About a dozen comets come into telescopic view every year, of which half have never been seen before. Discovering and naming comets has long been a favorite pastime of astronomers, especially amateur astronomers, who gain a certain amount of fame in the process and sometimes a minor fortune.

In the 1880's Edward E. Barnard, the American astronomer who would become famous for his discovery of Jupiter's innermost moon, was still young, poor, and an amateur. He was also newly married, and managed to make a two-hundred-dollar deposit on a modest house from the reward he received for discovering a comet. Thereafter, almost miraculously, whenever a mortgage payment came due, Barnard somehow discovered another comet, and, in the end, paid for his house entirely by comet-hunting.

In 1968 a sixteen-year-old Texas schoolboy discovered a comet at an amateur star-gazing party, but that kind of luck is very unusual. Leslie Peltier, a retired furniture designer in Ohio, has spent years watching for comets and shares the record of twelve discoveries with Minoru Honda, a Japanese farmer.

Another famous comet watcher is also Japanese: Kaoru Ikeya, who polishes keys in a Tokyo piano factory. Ikeya spotted his first comet at the age of nineteen during the night of January 2, 1963, using a six-inch reflecting telescope he had built himself at a cost of twenty-two dollars. The finding was the culmination of 109 nights of persistent observation. In September, 1965, Ikeya discovered a major comet (independently sighted by another young Japanese astronomer, Tsutomo Seki, and subse-quently named for both of them). Since then Ikeya has been discovering comets at the rate of about one a year.

While comet hunters continue to thrive, scientists are making special efforts to learn more about the anatomy of the comet. NASA's present long-range plans call for studies of comets by space vehicle, with one proposal in the offing for flying a probe through the tail of a comet. Space scientists say there is little likelihood of intercepting a long-period comet because its orbit is so different from that of the earth; one would need a good deal of rocket thrust available when a once-in-a-decade chance for rendezvous with a long-period comet arises. On the other hand, matching orbits with a short-period comet is possible every few years. Three comets will be in target position between 1969 and 1986, among them, the brilliant Halley's comet.

The basic objective in probing a comet directly is not just to learn more about these still mysterious natural space travelers, but more particularly because comets may provide us with valuable insights into the primordial state of the solar system. It seems unlikely for them to be forming at present, and almost impossible for them to come from interstellar space. So astronomers have tentatively concluded that they are condensations from the original solar nebula from which the planets formed, kept in deep freeze for billions of years. If so, the prospect of probing a comet, even if only by instrument, could mean that for the first time man would be able to make contact with a residuum of the dawn of the solar system.

Halley's comet is named after the 17th-century astronomer Edmund Halley, a pioneer in cometary research. Observing a particularly brilliant comet in 1682, Halley noticed that it moved in a path similar to those of comets that had been tracked 75 and 151 years earlier, and he concluded that the sightings were, in fact, of a single comet on a periodic orbit around the sun. Halley's comet is unusual in recurring within the span of a man's lifetime. Mark Twain (right) boasted that he came in with the comet (he was born in 1835) and he would go out with it. He died in 1910, the year of the comet's return— a truly spectacular affair, as this series of photographs shows.

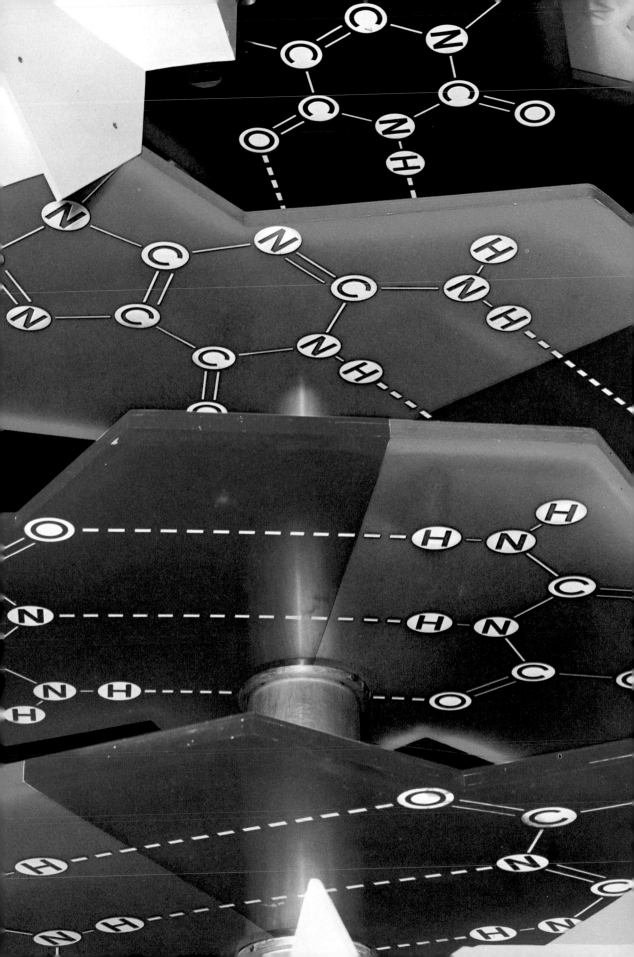

# 9. CAN THERE BE LIFE ELSEWHERE?

For hundreds of years man has been intrigued by the thought of extraterrestrial life, not just on the other worlds that revolve around our sun, but in the vast universe that lies beyond. Today, with plans afoot for exploring the solar system, we are on the verge of finding out at last whether man is unique in the universe or just one form of life among multitudes.

Since the seventh century B.C., when Thales, the father of Greek astronomy, concluded that the stars were made of the same material as earth and therefore must be inhabited in much the same way, philosophers and scientists have postulated that life elsewhere is probable. But for centuries after the coming of the Christian Era, the Church's rigid adherence to the Biblical view of a universe dominated by earth at its center stifled this philosophical questioning. Almost as effectively, the Church's strict interpretation of the Creation, as set forth in Genesis, repressed investigation by scientists of the origin of life.

By the late seventeenth century, however, Christian Huygens was presenting a teleological argument for life elsewhere, based on the principle of design, or direction toward an end. If the purpose of the earth was to support life, the purpose of each of the planets had to be identical, and therefore each one of them must also contain living creatures.

Huygens carried the idea a stage further with the argument that, since our sun is a star similar to others in the universe, "Why may not every one of these stars or suns have as great a retinue as our sun, of planets, with

*The "stairway" of life: detail from a model of the DNA molecule.*

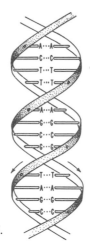

*Within the nucleus of each living cell are molecules of DNA (deoxyribonucleic acid), which ensure life's continuity. Each one is shaped like a double spiral staircase with twisting sides that are units of sugars and phosphates. The nitrogen compounds that form its steps are purines and pyrimidines, held together by hydrogen bonds, in a sequence that forms a code. The molecule duplicates itself by splitting apart; each strand then acts as a "mold" to form a molecule identical to the other strand.*

their moons, to wait upon them?" There was no reason, he felt, to suppose that the planets surrounding "that prodigious number of suns" should not also have "their plants and animals, nay and their rational creatures too, and those as great admirers, and as diligent observers of the heavens as ourselves."

Major advances in science during the eighteenth and nineteenth centuries brought with them the recasting of such arguments as scientific hypotheses. The lively and far-ranging debate over the possibility and probable form of life elsewhere gained a new dimension with the publication of Charles Darwin's *The Origin of Species* in 1859.

In this long and closely reasoned text, Darwin argued that the existing forms of life on earth had not been separately created but had evolved over many generations by natural selection. His thesis aroused a storm of protest, since it denied the idea of the separate creation of each species, as explicitly stated in the Bible. Darwin, concerned not with theology but with scientific evidence, rode out the storm. In putting forward the concept that there was a unity underlying all the visible differences in life forms on earth, he had opened up yet another area for discussion: If life could proceed from a single precursor, could not such a main event also have taken place elsewhere in the universe?

Some scientists as well as laymen adhered to the belief that the production of life on earth could only be an act of divine creation, though at a point far more distant in time than envisaged by the Bible. Others argued that life had probably originated solely through the opera-

tion of the laws of physics and chemistry. There were two variants of this view: one presumed that the origin of life had actually occurred on the earth; the other placed the event somewhere else in the universe and supposed that some fragment—a meteorite, perhaps—was responsible for depositing the first life on our planet.

Early in the twentieth century Svante Arrhenius, the Swedish chemist and Nobel Prize winner, proposed an ingenious variation of this last idea: that simple living things are constantly ejected into space from any habitable planets in the form of microscopic spores that are transported through space by radiation pressure and are able to impart life to any planet in a condition to receive them. These space-traveling spores he called panspermia.

But all such theories beg the really vital question—When and how did life originate in the first place?

From the point of view of today's biologists, one of the most astounding facts about all life on earth is that it consistently uses the same patterns—in its fundamental chemistry, in its genetic code, in its enzymes, and even in such apparently trivial matters as the molecules that are responsible for producing coloration. In a fundamental sense, the biologist finds himself studying only one organism—with minor variations among the different life forms, as, for example, between molds and men.

The reason for this astonishing similarity is likely to be that all earth's organisms have sprung from a single instance of the origin of life, an event that must have occurred in the

first billion years of earth's four-and-a-half-billion-year history. How can we date the origin of life so far back? Because the oldest earthly organisms, algae and bacteria that have been recovered from sediments laid down more than three billion years ago, closely resemble the fairly complex forms of modern algae and bacteria. The first life forms must have been far simpler, which means that life must have originated considerably longer ago than three billion years, and developed quite rapidly thereafter.

How did it originate? Apparently, from the most abundant atoms present in the universe. The earth's primordial atmosphere must have contained great quantities of hydrogen, which has subsequently escaped into space. The organic matter we ourselves are composed of is rich in hydrogen. In experiments, scientists have irradiated or sent a spark through hydrogen-rich gases typical of those present on the primitive earth. This produces organic molecules in substantial quantities—amino acids, sugars, purines, and pyrimidines, the fundamental building blocks of contemporary biochemistry. These same molecules are in part responsible for the remarkable uniformity of life on earth.

On this thin experimental reed, buttressed by plausible assumption, scientists have built the story of life, seeing it as emerging at some point in the first billion years of earth's history from the primordial ocean and atmosphere in the form of a self-replicating DNA molecule, the master substance of heredity, and then growing and diversifying through countless mutations over another three and a half billion years into the abundance of natural forms we see about us today. The common ancestry of living things postulated by Darwin is in effect proved by the twentieth-century biologists' discovery of their chemical similarity.

Interestingly, although in his published work Darwin made no guesses about the origin of life, he did privately speculate on the possibility of the chemical origin of a protein compound "in some warm little pond, with all sorts of ammonia and phosphoric salts, light, heat, electricity, etc., present."

The modern view on how life arose from the nonliving world was formulated by the Russian biochemist A. I. Oparin in the 1930's. He envisioned the synthesis of organic molecules into a life system without the intervention of an *élan vital*, a spark of life, and laid the groundwork for the present philosophy of the chemical origin of life based on the nature of the primitive earth.

The theory suggests the possibility that life may arise elsewhere under similar conditions and using the common materials of the universe. Could other molecules, created by energy in the same fashion, have led to very different sorts of life on other worlds, inside or outside our solar system? No one has succeeded in synthesizing a living organism of "our" type, so no biologist knows whether other varieties might also be possible. It is a relatively speedy affair to carry out experiments on the chemistry of the origin of life, but experiments into life's evolution are incredibly time-consuming because such very large numbers of

The galaxy M 31 in the constellation Andromeda is seen through Mount Palomar's 48-inch Schmidt telescope, a wide-angle camera. M 31, some 2 million light-years away, is the nearest spiral galaxy to our own Milky Way and like it has some 150 billion stars. A few of our galaxy's stars sprinkle the foreground. There are so many stars in the billions of galaxies in the universe that even if life-bearing planets are rare there must be an enormous number of possible abodes for life.

generations must come into being, live, and die before any significant evolution occurs. This is one reason why the search for extraterrestrial life, even in its simplest forms, has such great appeal. Will life forms from other planets contain nucleic acids as the basis of their genetic code? Will their enzymes be proteins? Will they be built out of cells similar to ours? Will they look like any terrestrial organisms? We can answer these basic questions only by direct observation of extraterrestrial life.

As we have seen, attempts to detect the possible presence of life on Mars are currently being planned, and in the period from now until the early 1970's, when the orbits of Mars and the earth are at their closest, both the Soviet Union and the United States will almost certainly try to land life-detecting instruments on the planet. Similar searches in the more exotic environment of Venus and journeys to the region around Jupiter should follow before too long.

What about the possibility of life in other parts of the universe? Ever since Edwin Powell Hubble began systematically observing the great galaxies lying at vast distances beyond our own Milky Way, we have known that our own little planet lies in one corner of one galaxy of 150,000 million stars. If life began in such an obscure place, runs the argument, why not elsewhere? Statistically, can we be the only civilization in the universe?

As Harlow Shapley of Harvard has put it: "It is hopelessly vain to believe that we are something special and superior in the universe of more than 100,000 million billion stars. It is gratifying to be part of this magnificent evolutionary show, even though we must admit to be lineal descendants of rather nauseating gases and sundry streaks of lightning."

In the last few decades we have achieved a technical civilization capable of interstellar communication. Our large radio telescopes can transmit intelligible information over enormous distances—hundreds of light-years across the emptiness between the stars. The nearest stars are only a little over four light-years from earth, and there must be something like one million within the volume that our radio telescopes can penetrate. What are the chances of our entering into communication with a civilization on the planet of some other star?

They depend on a number of factors, all of them more or less problematical, such as the rate of star formation, the number of planets per star, and the number of planets per solar system that are suitable for the origin of life. There can only be a fraction of such planets on which life actually originates, a still smaller fraction where it evolves into an intelligent species, and an even smaller fraction on which that species develops a technical civilization that is capable of communication. Perhaps the most enigmatic factor of all is the possible lifetime of such a technical civilization—by the time its signal had been received and returned across the great gulf of space, a civilization might have ceased to exist.

A typical rough estimate, however, projects that one out of every hundred thousand stars in the universe currently has a technical civilization at or beyond our own level of techno-

logical advancement, with which we might be able to communicate.

So far only one serious attempt has been made to detect intelligent radio communications from the vicinity of another star. Called Project Ozma, after the princess of the mysterious land of Oz, it was organized in 1959 by Frank Drake of Cornell University, who was then at the National Radio Astronomy Observatory at Green Bank, West Virginia.

Drake and his group decided to focus on a single frequency—that emitted by interstellar hydrogen—partly because it might be familiar to extraterrestrial astronomers, but chiefly because their telescope was equipped to receive it. Two likely stars were chosen for the test—Tau Ceti, in the constellation Cetus, the Whale, and Epsilon Eridani, in the constellation Eridanus, the River. Both these stars are some ten light-years away, resemble our sun, and may further resemble it in being ringed by planets.

For several months during 1960 the astronomers focused their radio dish at the chosen pair of stars. Almost at once they detected a signal, and grew quite excited. In fact, the same signal appeared twice, but on closer investigation it proved disappointingly to be from an earthly source, connected with secret military radar experiments. They finally had to conclude that nobody was signaling at that time, from those stars, at that particular frequency.

Drake is still optimistic, however, and would like to try again. "There are many more stars farther out and this was only the first attempt," he says. The project was significant, neverthe-less, because it was the first time a radio search for extraterrestrial life had been made in earnest; in some form, the search must soon be taken up again.

Although such efforts to detect life beyond our planet have been unsuccessful, there are many people who believe that the inhabitants of other worlds have already contacted us and that we are in fact being visited by them constantly. Reports of Unidentified Flying Objects (UFO's) have recently been reassessed both by Air Force investigators and by an independent team of scientists. The consensus of opinion is that such sightings are largely misapprehended natural phenomena, with a smattering of hoaxes and cases of actual self-deception. A number of observations are still unexplained, however, and although there is no direct evidence establishing them as sightings of space vehicles from other planets, believers will no doubt continue to point to them as examples of extraterrestrial visitation. For the time being, the question can only remain an open one.

Before we enter a new century we shall probably be in possession of at least some of the answers to the age-old quest for life and intelligence beyond the earth. The solar system looms forth with new worlds for man to conquer; he has the instruments at hand, he has the ability to interpret their readings. We are on the threshold of learning where and how things began, both in the solar system and in the universe beyond, and of achieving an awareness deeper than ever before of man's place in that universe.

# APPENDIX

# HIGHLIGHTS IN
# PLANETARY ASTRONOMY

## MERCURY

**c. 530 B.C.** *The followers of Pythagoras, the Greek philosophermathematician, are the first to teach that the earth is spherical.*

**c. 350 B.C.** *Heraclides, Greek astronomer, suggests that the earth rotates about its axis and that at least some of the planets might revolve about the sun.*

**c. 260 B.C.** *Aristarchus of Samos carries Heraclides' idea a stage further and proposes that the sun is the center of the universe.*

**A.D. 127-151** *Ptolemy of Alexandria establishes the first complete mathematical model for the solar system in his* Almagest, *in which he develops the idea of an earthcentered universe around which the planets and the sun revolve.*

**1543** *Copernicus, Polish astronomer, publishes* De Revolutionibus Orbium Celestium, *which revives the ancient ideas of Aristarchus in postulating a sun-centered universe. Copernicus also determines the positions of the five known planets and calculates their orbital periods.*

**1563-1601** *Tycho Brahe, Danish astronomer, makes accurate instrumented observations of the planets.*

**1609** *Johannes Kepler, German astronomer, publishes his* Astronomia Nova, *containing his First and Second Laws of Planetary Motion, which explain the apparent motions of the planets. Ten years later he publishes his Third Law of Planetary Motion.*

**1609** *The age of telescopic astronomy begins as the Italian scientist Galileo Galilei constructs a telescope that enables him to identify upland and lowland areas on the moon. He also notes the phases of Venus, and finds that Jupiter has four satellites.*

**1610** *Johannes Fabricius, Christoph Scheiner, Thomas Harriot, and Galileo all observe sunspots through their telescopes.*

**1655** *Christian Huygens, Dutch astronomer, discovers Saturn's first moon. In 1656 he notes that the planet is surrounded by a thin ring.*

## VENUS

## EARTH

**1668** *At Cambridge, England, Isaac Newton designs the first reflecting telescope. Unlike Galileo's telescope, which focuses refracted light through a lens, the Newtonian model concentrates light by reflection from a curved mirror.*

**1671-1684** *Jean Dominique Cassini, a Franco-Italian astronomer, discovers four more satellites orbiting Saturn and observes a dark gap in Saturn's ring, now known as the Cassini division.*

**1687** *Isaac Newton's Law of Universal Gravitation is published in his* Principia. *From this simple, fundamental formula, all the motions of the solar system can be calculated.*

**1705** *Edmund Halley, English astronomer, predicts that the comet he saw in 1682 will reappear in 1758. Because of some small errors in calculation, it actually appeared in 1759. The comet is named for Halley, who demonstrated that comets, like planets, have elliptical orbits and are gravitationally bound to the sun.*

**1755**  *In his* General History of Nature and Theory of the Heavens *Immanuel Kant, German philosopher, sets forth a nebular hypothesis for the origin of the solar system. In 1796, Pierre, Marquis de Laplace independently suggests a similar hypothesis.*

**1781**  *William Herschel, English astronomer, discovers the planet Uranus. Later he notes a glowing spot on the moon, which he attributes to volcanic activity, and discovers two of Uranus' satellites.*

**1789**  *Herschel directs his newly designed 48-inch reflector telescope at Saturn and discovers two more satellites.*

**1801**  *At Palermo, Italy, Giuseppi Piazzi discovers the first asteroid and names it Ceres.*

**1842**  *Christian Johann Doppler, Austrian physicist, discovers that when a radiating object races toward or away from an observer there is a shift in frequency of the radiation, a phenomenon since known as the Doppler effect.*

MARS

JUPITER

**1843**  *Heinrich Schwabe, German astronomer, discovers that sunspots wax and wane on a cyclical basis.*

**1845–1846**  *John Couch Adams and Urbain Jean Joseph Leverrier, English and French astronomers, independently calculate the position of an unknown planet from irregularities in the motion of Uranus. German astronomer Johann G. Galle finds Neptune on the basis of Leverrier's calculations.*

**1846**  *William Lassell, English astronomer, discovers the first of Neptune's two known satellites, and in 1851 two more of Uranus' satellites, bringing the total to four.*

**1857**  *James Clerk Maxwell, Scottish physicist, proves theoretically that Saturn's ring is composed of quantities of individual particles.*

**1869–1872**  *Laurence, Earl of Rosse measures lunar radiation using a 3-foot reflector combined with a thermopile. In the mid-1880's, American astronomers Samuel Langley and Frank Very observe the moon with a radiometer.*

**1877**  *Asaph Hall, American astronomer, discovers Mars' two moons, and Giovanni Schiaparelli, Italian astronomer, detects fine lines on Mars' surface, which he calls* canali.

**1889**  *American scientist George Ellery Hale invents the spectroheliograph, a device that makes it possible to photograph the sun in a single wavelength of light.*

**1892**  *The fifth of Jupiter's satellites is discovered by American astronomer Edward E. Barnard.*

**1894**  *Fascinated by Schiaparelli's reports of canals on Mars, Percival Lowell establishes an observatory in Flagstaff, Arizona, for planetary research.*

**1930**  *Working at Flagstaff with Lowell's calculations, American astronomer Clyde Tombaugh discovers Pluto, the outermost planet in our solar system.*

**1930**  *Bernard Lyot, French astronomer, invents the coronagraph, a device that permits the solar*

SATURN

## URANUS

corona to be viewed by artificially eclipsing the sun.

**1930** *Edison Pettit and Seth Nicholson, American astronomers, make the first reliable determinations of lunar temperature by measuring infrared radiation.*

**1931** *Karl Jansky, an engineer at Bell Telephone Laboratories, detects radio waves emanating from outer space. His discovery marks the birth of radio astronomy.*

**1931** *German-born astronomer Rupert Wildt suggests that the dark bands that show up on spectrograms of Jupiter probably represent the gases methane and ammonia.*

**1932** *A spectroscopic study by Walter Adams and Theodore Dunham identifies large amounts of carbon dioxide in the atmosphere of Venus.*

**1946** *The U.S. Army Signal Corps bounces radar waves off the moon, the first use of radar in solar system astronomy.*

**1949** *Dutch-American astronomer Gerard Kuiper discovers carbon dioxide in the atmosphere of Mars.*

**1955** *Kenneth Franklin and Bernard Burke find that Jupiter is an intense source of radio emission.*

**1956** *Cornell Mayer and his colleagues discover that Venus is a strong source of radio emission.*

**1959** *The Soviet Union's Luna 2 crash-lands on the moon, becoming the first man-made object to land on a celestial body.*

**1962** *U.S. spacecraft Mariner 2 flies past Venus and discovers considerably greater microwave intensity at the planet's surface than in the ionosphere.*

**1964** *Mariner 4 leaves earth on a trip to Mars. The spacecraft flies by the planet in July, 1965, and sends back 22 pictures taken from a distance of 6,118 miles above its surface. Mariner 4 also finds the Martian atmospheric pressure 1 per cent that of the earth.*

## NEPTUNE

P

## PLUTO

**1964–1965** *Roland Carpenter and Richard Goldstein discover by radar techniques that Venus rotates in the opposite direction to its revolution, with a period of about 243 days. Rolf Dyce and Gordon Pettengill, using similar techniques, find that Mercury rotates in the same direction as its revolution, with a period of about 59 days.*

**1966** *Audouin Dollfus, French astronomer, discovers the tenth and currently the last of Saturn's satellites.*

**1966** *Soviet spacecraft Luna 9 makes the first soft landing on the moon and sends back the first close-up photographs of the lunar surface.*

**1967** *The Soviet Venera 4 enters the Venerean atmosphere, measuring temperatures, pressures, and composition.*

**1968** *The U.S. Apollo 8 returns the first color photographs of the earth and moon taken by men in lunar orbit.*

# TELESCOPES:
# MAN'S WINDOW
# INTO SPACE

The optical telescope has transformed man's outlook on the skies. The fact that glass can be shaped to extend the limits of our vision is in itself a wonder. As early as the 3rd century B.C., Egyptian craftsmen discovered how to "anneal" glass by melting and bending it into different shapes. Crudely devised magnifying lenses were being used as visual aids in 13th-century Europe. But there could be no real accuracy in a lens until men realized that glass had to be ground following the principle of light refraction. This discovery and the refinements it made possible created a flourishing spectacle-making industry in Holland in the 16th century. It was a Dutch spectaclemaker—his identity is still in dispute—who, early in the 1600's, invented the refracting telescope.

Telescopes were first conceived of as toys, and sold as such. Once Galileo and other astronomers had realized their amazing utility as scientific instruments, however, technical improvements followed rapidly. But from the first tiny spyglass to today's giant devices, telescopes share the magic quality that drew the Victorian children above to a London street corner: they offer man a window into the infinite reaches of space.

*A 17th-century aerial telescope—a refractor with*

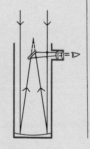

All optical telescopes are based on one or other of light's two well-known properties: that it can be refracted or reflected. Light is refracted, or bent, when it passes at an oblique angle from one transparent medium, such as air, into one of a different density, such as glass. When light passes through a lens, it is bent and brought to a focus, where it forms an image. In the diagram at upper left, light enters a refracting telescope through the objective lens at top and is bent so that the image at the focus (where the lines cross) is seen upside down and reversed by the eye beneath. The eyepiece, acting like a miniature microscope, enlarges the image; the objective lens gathers and focuses the light.

The drawback of the refracting telescope is that light is composed of different colors of varying wavelengths, and that each color is bent at a different angle. Consequently, the refractor cannot bring the images in each color to the same focus—a failing known as chromatic aberration.

Isaac Newton hit upon the idea that when light is reflected it does not pass through glass, and can thus produce an image free from chromatic aberration. The telescope he designed is diagramed at lower left. Its objective is a concave mirror at the base of the tube that bounces light back up the tube to the focus. A flat mirror placed below the focus reflects light out at right angles through the hole at right, where it is magnified by the eyepiece. The objective mirror is ground and polished to a parabolic surface that is then coated with silver or aluminum. (Unlike regular mirrors, the telescopic mirror is silvered on the front surface, not the back.) When a Newtonian telescope is used for photography, the flat secondary mirror is removed and the photographic plates are placed at the focus within the tube. This is known as the prime focus—that is, the focal point that would be reached if the secondary mirror did not intervene.

A further improvement in the reflecting telescope occurred when Guillaume Cassegrain, a 17th-century French scientist, increased its focal length without increasing its physical length. (The focal length is the distance between the objective and the point at which the focus is formed; the image can be enlarged either by

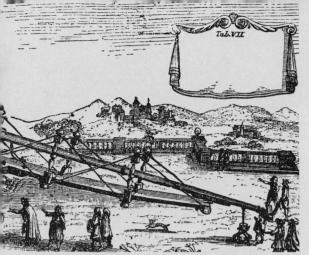

*a 75-foot focal length—is hoisted by block and tackle.*

increasing the focal length or by using an eyepiece with higher magnification.) Cassegrain's reflector is diagramed at upper right. In this case, the objective mirror, the primary, which is placed at the base of the tube, collects light and reflects it up toward the focus. But the secondary, a convex mirror below the focus, reflects light back down the tube, forcing it through a hole in the primary to the eyepiece. The optical effect of this secondary is to double or triple the equivalent focal length of the telescope, with a consequent enlargement of the image.

The coudé telescope is also a French design—as might be expected from its name, which means elbowed—and it was first used at the Paris Observatory in the late 19th century. It came into being because of the extreme discomfort of observing in the old-fashioned style. A prime requisite for effective observing is transparency of the atmosphere, which means that great observatories are usually built on mountaintops, and the best conditions for viewing most often occur in winter. The result is that astronomers frequently have to dress like arctic explorers. The eyepiece of the coudé is in a heated observation room, rather than outdoors with the rest of the equipment, enabling the observer to work in some comfort—and sitting down.

Modern reflectors, such as the 200-inch Hale telescope, use a form of coudé focus, usually combined with a Cassegrain arrangement. As shown in the diagram at lower right, light is gathered by means of a parabolic mirror at the base of the tube; the light is reflected up to the secondary and then down to a flat mirror that bends it and sends it out, at right angles, to the eyepiece.

The steady sophistication of contemporary telescopes has been accompanied by refinement in photographic techniques. Today, the world's great telescopes are chiefly used for taking photographs, whose long exposures can concentrate light from low-magnitude stars too dim to form an effective image for the eye. Using a 48-inch Schmidt camera—a telescope that combines a spherical mirror with a corrector plate to get the effect of a wide-angle lens without the off-focus distortion—astronomers at Mount Palomar have made a complete survey of the visible northern skies.

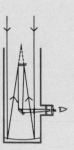

One of the first men to investigate the optical use of lenses was Roger Bacon (below), a 13th-century English scholar. Some historians believe he may even have built a crude telescope, but no instrument survives. Two of the earliest known telescopes, created by Galileo some 350 years later, are displayed at left. They were simple refracting lens arrangements, similar to the modern opera glass, but their images were marred by a prismatic effect that blurred them with a halo of colors. Christian Huygens, the brilliant Dutch astronomer, designed the aerial telescope at right in an attempt to reduce such chromatic aberration by using a long-focus objective lens. Instead of housing it in a tube, he mounted the lens on a platform that slid up and down a pole when the observer, standing by the eyepiece, pulled a string taut. This aligned the two lenses—which could be up to 210 feet apart—and adjusted the position of the focus.

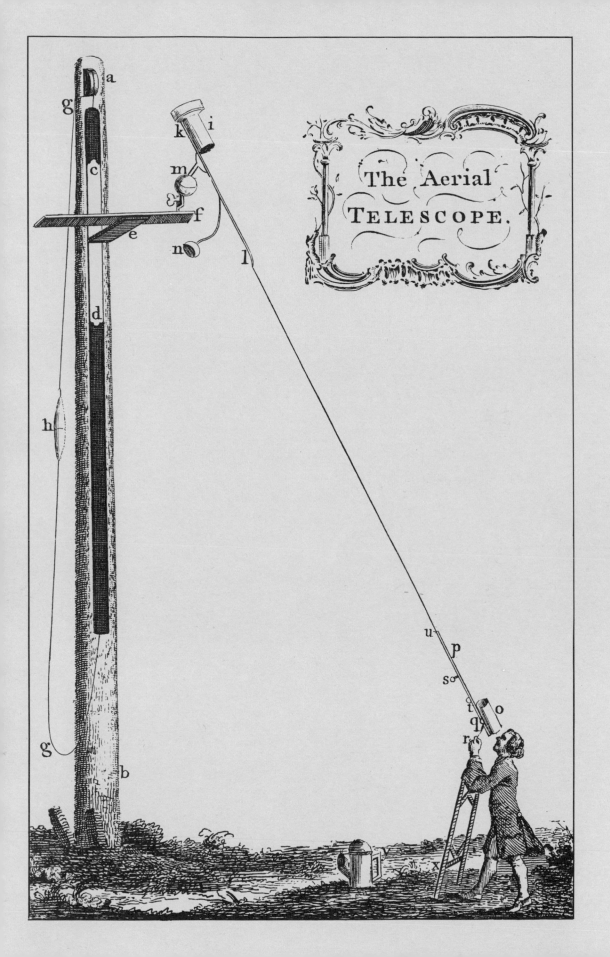

The Aerial
TELESCOPE.

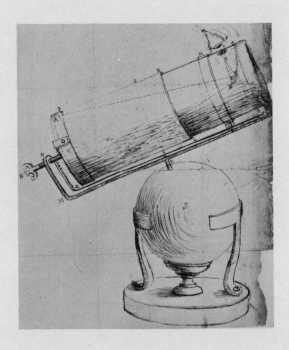

The Newtonian reflector, devised by the brilliant
scientist in 1668 after many optical experiments,
is shown in this drawing, presented to the Royal Society in 1672. To solve the problem of chromatic
aberration, Newton moved the eyepiece up the
tube to the side and fitted a mirror into the base
of the tube to reflect light back up to the focus.
This type of reflecting telescope was redesigned a
century later by William Herschel, who dispensed
with the side reflector altogether. Instead he tilted
the mirror at the base of his front-view tube so
that its light was brought to a focus at the upper
rim of the tube. With the eyepiece at the top of the
tube, he could stand on a balcony just below and
view the image. Herschel's crowning achievement was
the giant reflecting telescope at left, with a 40-foot
focal length. The five-story framework supported
a vast iron tube, which housed a 48-inch mirror,
the largest of its time. The mounting of the mirror
itself was a further feat, since it weighed more than
a ton. It was made of cast speculum metal, an alloy
much used in the 18th century because it would take
a high polish. Because of the risk of ruining the
mirror's figure (its optical shape), repolishing it
when it tarnished could be tricky for lesser men
than Herschel, who was a master of lens-making.

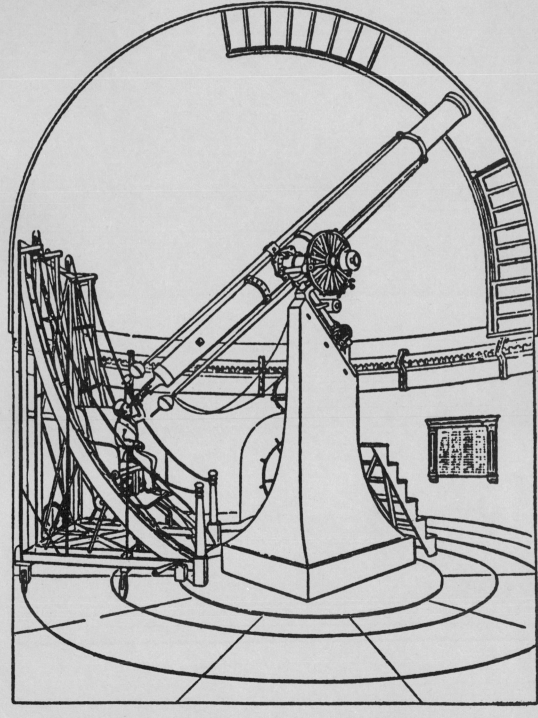

*Joseph von Fraunhofer (far left)
died before he was 40 but left
an indelible imprint on astronomy.
In the early 19th century, it was
he who revitalized the refracting telescope by contriving to polish lenses and mirrors without
altering their curvature. This work
led him to make the first observations of dark lines in the solar
spectrum, and his discoveries were
later developed by Gustav Kirchhoff
(near left) into the science of
spectroscopy, a major tool of astronomical research. Fraunhofer was
also one of the first astronomers
to understand the importance of
solid mounts for his instruments.
The Harvard refractor (below, left)
is a copy of his classic design.
Problems with mounts sometimes
received more fanciful solutions,
as in the short-focus reflector at
right, devised by Léon Jobert, a
19th-century Parisian astronomer.*

The coudé telescope at left, being
used at the Paris Observatory
by an astronomer in an easy chair,
was installed there around 1883.
Before the invention of the coudé,
the comforts of the observer had fall-
en far behind the steady improvement in accuracy of his observations.
This particular instrument is equatorially mounted—a design that
aligns the principal axis of the
mount with due north, giving the
instrument greater stability
and allowing the astronomer to track
his object without having to shift
his own position. Another advantage
of the coudé focus is that spectroscopic or photoelectric equipment
can be set up in the room alongside
the eyepiece without altering
the position of the external telescope; today, in fact, the coudé
is chiefly used for spectrography.

George Ellery Hale (above, left) was a brilliant astronomer who invented the spectroheliograph, a device used by most investigators of the sun today. It enables astronomers to view or photograph the sun through a single narrow band of the spectrum with the light emitted by a single element. Hale also had special talents as a fund raiser and was instrumental in the creation of the great Yerkes Observatory refractor, the 100-inch reflector on Mount Wilson, and the 200-inch reflector on Mount Palomar, which now bears his name. The Hale reflector (diagramed below) is not only the largest but probably the most versatile optical telescope in the world: it can be used as a Newtonian instrument for photography at the prime focus and as a long-focus coudé telescope for spectrographic work. There is also a Cassegrain focus, piercing the giant mirror. The telescope's horseshoe mounting gives it access to the north polar regions of the sky, which is denied to the more conventional equatorially mounted reflectors. It works with such precision that it can be trained on distant stars for exposures of up to seven hours, taken over an interrupted period, without any loss of clarity. At right, the observatory shutters are open, revealing the observer's cage at prime focus (center) and beyond it the wooded terrain of Mount Palomar.

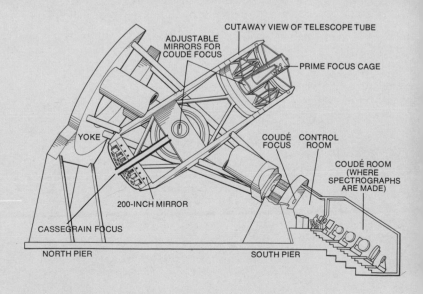

# THE SEARCH FOR PLANET X

The story appeared in the morning papers on Friday, March 14, 1930. A new planet, the ninth in the solar system, had been discovered by Clyde W. Tombaugh, a photographer at Lowell Observatory in Flagstaff, Arizona. Its finding was the culmination of a 25-year program begun by the noted astronomer Percival Lowell, the observatory's founder. He calculated from irregularities in the motion of Neptune that it must be gravitationally influenced by another planet beyond it in the solar system. Attempts to make a systematic photographic search for such a planet, however, were unrewarding, and when Lowell died in 1916 the project was broken off. Then in 1929, with greatly improved instruments at hand, the Lowell astronomers resumed the search and assigned 23-year-old Clyde Tombaugh to it as photographic assistant.

The son of a farming family in Kansas, Tombaugh had an avid interest in astronomy but not enough money to go to college. Instead, he built himself a 9-inch telescope, largely out of old farm equipment, and studied the skies on his own. He sent some of his observational drawings of Mars and Jupiter to the Lowell Observatory, and these so impressed its director, V. M. Slipher, that he offered Tombaugh a job on the Planet X program, where an observer was needed to do the night work.

The position of Planet X was calculated to be in the constellation Gemini, where it would appear as a dim star in the company of many other dim stars, distinguished from them only by its movement, which at such a distance would be barely perceptible. Tombaugh worked for hours on end, photographing the sky simultaneously through a new 13-inch refractor and a 5-inch camera mounted on the larger telescope's tube. Each exposure took at least an hour to make; then, several nights later, each area would have to be rephotographed under conditions that were as closely similar as possible.

The next step was to examine the plates in a blink microscope, a device in which two matching plates taken on different nights are illuminated in quick succession. The principle is the same as that of the motion picture: any object that has changed position in the interval seems to move or "blink." Looking for a minute sign of movement on plates containing hundreds of thousands of stars, however, was tedious indeed; often it took days to blink just one pair.

Tombaugh persisted, nonetheless, and on February 18, 1930, found a minute speck that moved. It was Planet X—known to us now as Pluto. Thirty years later, Tombaugh, who had become a well-known planetary astronomer, recalled the events of his discovery:

By April, 1929, the actual observations began, with the first preliminary photographs being taken of the Gemini region, then sinking into the western sky, [which] was the area favored by Lowell to contain his Planet X. As regions farther east were observed, it became evident that most of the planet suspects were within one magnitude of the 13-inch limit and beyond the help of the 5-inch. Therefore, the practice was adopted of taking three good plates per center within a few nights of each other (preferably all three in a week). The two best-matching plates were compared in the blink microscope, and the third was available as an immediate check on any suspected moving object.

This procedure made it practical to push a thorough search well into the 17th magnitude. Chance aggregations of silver grains near the plate limit gave rise to thousands of planet suspects over the years. Each had to be checked, for the risk could not be taken of letting the long-sought planet slip by. Many suspicious images turned out to be faint variable stars whose minima were fainter than the plate limit.

That summer several astronomers passing through Flagstaff were shown the 13-inch telescope and informed of its search program. One of them said frankly that looking for trans-Neptunian planets was a waste of time and effort, since so much prior work had been without success. But we knew that the 13-inch was the best-suited instrument yet brought to bear on the problem.

During the dark of the moon, 10 to 15 hours of observing and dark-room work were required daily to run two search strips parallel to the ecliptic concurrently. [The ecliptic is the apparent path of the sun around the celestial sphere.] Adhering strictly to the opposition regions eliminated the asteroid problem entirely, for every minor planet exhibited a definite trail during the hour exposure, and was displaced about seven millimeters per day.

As the autumn of 1929 came, the perfected technique of observing and blink examination had settled into routine. When the plates were well matched and reasonably clean of spurious images, I could carry out six or seven hours of actual blinking each day. In Pisces and Aries, each plate recorded some 50,000 stars, and a pair could be examined in three days. These plates were a delight to scan, with hundreds of images of beautiful spiral galaxies.

The number of star images gradually increased as the Milky Way was approached. The plates of eastern Taurus and western Gemini contained up to 400,000 stars each! These had to be examined in small

*In a front-page story for March 14, 1930, The New York Times headlines the new planet's discovery. Ironically, it is now thought Lowell's calculations led to the finding of Pluto only by a lucky chance.*

groups of only a dozen stars at a time. For very rich regions, it was necessary to use narrow rectangular diaphragms to limit the maze of stars. Therefore, the speed of examination decreased as these rich star regions were encountered, and the work with the blink comparator began to fall behind schedule.

In February, 1930, after struggling through the Taurus plates, I skipped over to those in eastern Gemini, where the stars were less thickly packed. The entire length of the latter constellation had been photographed by the end of January that year. I chose three plates centered on Delta Geminorum, taken January 21st, 23rd, and 29th, respectively, but bad seeing made the first of these unacceptable for blinking.

I placed the other two in the comparator and began blinking the east half from the south end. By 4:00 P.M. on February 18th, one-fourth of the plate area had been blinked. Upon turning to a new eyepiece field two-thirds of a degree east of Delta, I suddenly spied a 15th-magnitude object popping in and out of the background. Just three-and-a-half millimeters away another 15th-magnitude image was doing the same thing, but appearing alternately with respect to the other, as first one plate and then the second was visible through the eyepiece.

"That's it!" I exclaimed to myself. The change in position—only three or four millimeters in six days—was much too small for an ordinary asteroid near opposition. But were the images real or spurious? At once I laid out the [5-inch camera plates taken] simultaneously with the 13-inch exposures. Although nearly at its limit of visibility, there were the images exactly in the same respective positions!

With mounting excitement, I got out the January 21st plates and quickly checked them with a hand magnifier. Even though the 13-inch plate was a sorry one, there was the image displaced about one millimeter east of the January 23rd position, and it was confirmed on the 5-inch exposure. Any possibility of the phenomenon being a pair of variable stars was now ruled out. Next, I measured the displacements approximately with a millimeter scale. The object was retrograding about 70 seconds of arc per day. This seemed to be it!

Dr. Lampland [one of the staff astronomers] was in his office across the hall. At 4:45 P.M., I told him that I had found something, and he came in and sat down at the comparator. Then I went to the director's office to inform Dr. Slipher, who hurried down the hall to the comparator room. . . . The two astronomers repeated the same checks for their satisfaction. The air was tense with excitement. We looked through the window. The sky was very cloudy—no chance of getting a recovery plate that evening. Dr. Slipher stressed that no announcement should be made until observational confirmation was completed during the next few weeks.

I was a young bachelor then, and generally left the observatory at 5 P.M. to go downtown for dinner. But it must have been after six o'clock when we dispersed from the comparator room. I could hardly eat for thinking about the images. I remember that because the evening was cloudy, I went to the movies and saw Gary Cooper in *The Virginian*. After the gun-drawing act, I came out tenser than ever. It was still cloudy.

The next night, February 19th, was clear, and another one-hour exposure of the Delta Geminorum region could be taken. I developed the plate and left it on the drying rack to be ready for blinking the next morning with one of the discovery pair. Although three weeks had elapsed, the new image was quickly found about one centimeter west of the January 29th position. . . .

As the weeks passed, the motion of the object conformed perfectly to that expected of a trans-Neptunian planet. It was decided to announce the discovery on March 13, 1930, which was the 75th anniversary of Percival Lowell's birth, and the date of Uranus' discovery 149 years earlier. Late on the night of the 12th, director V. M. Slipher sent a telegram to the Harvard Observatory clearinghouse for official distribution.

Next day the news spread out over the world. Soon newspaper and magazine reporters arrived in Flagstaff and swarmed over the observatory on Mars Hill. Letters and telegrams poured in containing congratulations and suggesting names for the new planet. Around the observatory all other work was disrupted. Observers at other institutions quickly confirmed the position and motion of the new planet.

Of the names suggested, the three most popular were Pluto, Minerva, and Cronus. However, one of the asteroids had already been called after Minerva, the goddess of wisdom. Pluto was better known, and his fellow gods Jupiter and Saturn were already in the heavens. In early May, the name Pluto was selected by Lowell Observatory and officially proposed to the American Astronomical Society and to the Royal Astronomical Society. For the planetary symbol, the interlocked letters P and L were chosen, being both the first two letters of the planet's name and Percival Lowell's initials.

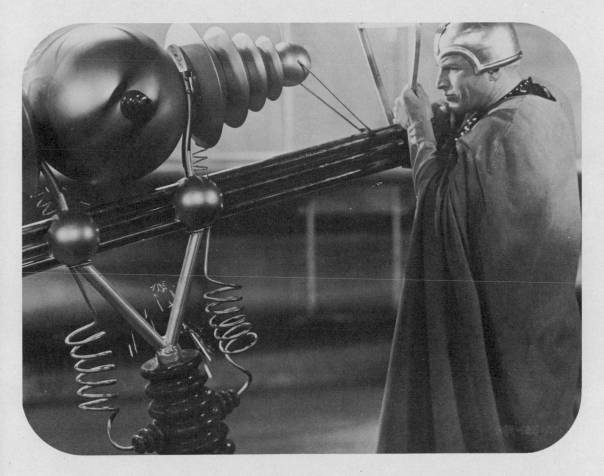

*One currently popular product of man's eternal curiosity about space is science fiction, a colorful form of speculation in literature, television, and motion pictures. Authors of science fiction have never agreed on how to define the genre or the extent to which it differs from fantasy. All, however, are united in contempt for "space opera"—their term for any hackneyed adventure story given a spuriously scientific air by the mechanical process of replacing cattle rustlers with extraterrestrial aliens or monsters, transforming cowboy suits into space suits, and substituting death rays for six-shooters. Such movie space operas as Mars Attacks the World (above) feature classic clichés: the mysterious machine like an X-ray tube on giant bedsprings and the Romanoid cloak and helmet essential to all bona fide invaders.*

Trip to the Moon, *1902*

Flash Gordon Conquers
the Universe, *1940*

Rocket Ship, *1950*

*The Parisian spoof* Trip to the
Moon *was the precursor of a spate
of Hollywood science fiction movies
aimed at the eternal adolescent.
Translating Robin Hood–Maid
Marian situations into space opera
proved lucrative, but the burlap-
legged monsters of* Invaders from
Mars *(right) typify the approach.
The adult art form began with
the filming of* Destination Moon.

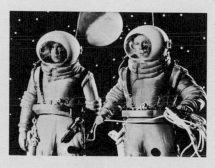

Destination Moon, *1950*

A recent, outstanding attempt to bring authentic science fiction to the screen was 2001: A Space Odyssey, by Stanley Kubrick and Arthur C. Clarke. It took three years to film the special effects, a few of which are shown here. Below, a 700-foot nuclear-powered spaceship sets out to investigate the possibility of extraterrestrial intelligence in the region near Jupiter; space "pods" are released from the ship on small excursions; during a "space walk" an astronaut's oxygen line is cut and his body is lost in space; at right, a comrade, risking explosive decompression by entering space without his protective suit and mask, careens wildly inside the ship's air lock. Kubrick and Clarke make no compromises with space opera clichés; the only "bad guy" is a demented computer.

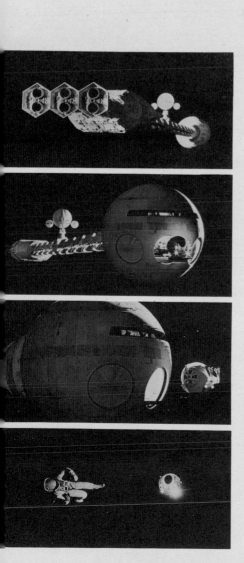

# FURTHER READING

*Asterisk indicates paperback edition.*

## GENERAL

Alter, Dinsmore, et al. *Pictorial Astronomy* (2nd rev. ed.). New York: Thomas Y. Crowell Company, 1963.

Coleman, James A. *Modern Theories of the Universe.* New York: New American Library, Inc., 1963.*

Jastrow, Robert. *Red Giants and White Dwarfs: The Evolution of Stars, Planets and Life.* New York: Harper & Row, Publishers, 1967.

Shapley, Harlow (ed.). *A Source Book in Astronomy, 1900–1950.* Cambridge: Harvard University Press, 1960.

Shklovskii, Iosif S., and Carl Sagan. *Intelligent Life in the Universe.* San Francisco: Holden-Day, Inc., 1966.*

Struve, Otto, et al. *Elementary Astronomy.* New York: Oxford University Press, 1959.

Sullivan, Walter. *We Are Not Alone* (rev. ed.). New York: McGraw-Hill Book Company, Inc., 1966.*

## HISTORY AND BIOGRAPHY

Armitage, Angus. *The World of Copernicus.* New York: New American Library, Inc., 1951.*

Armitage, Angus. *William Herschel.* Garden City, N.Y.: Doubleday & Company, Inc., 1962.

Bixby, William. *The Universe of Galileo and Newton.* New York: American Heritage Publishing Co., Inc., 1964.

Casper, Max. *Kepler.* New York: Abelard-Schuman Limited, 1959.*

Coleman, James A. *Early Theories of the Universe.* New York: New American Library, Inc., 1967.*

Hoyle, Fred. *Astronomy.* Garden City, N.Y.: Doubleday & Company, Inc., 1962.

Koestler, Arthur. *The Sleepwalkers.* New York: Crowell Collier and Macmillan, Inc., 1959.

Ley, Willy. *Watchers of the Skies.* New York: The Viking Press, Inc., 1963.

Moore, Patrick. *Picture History of Astronomy.* New York: Grosset & Dunlap, Inc., 1961.

Stillman, Drake (ed.). *Discoveries and Opinions of Galileo.* Garden City, N.Y.: Doubleday & Company, Inc., 1957.*

Struve, Otto, and Velta Zebergs. *Astronomy of the 20th Century.* New York: Crowell Collier and Macmillan, Inc., 1962.

Thiel, Rudolf. *And There Was Light.* New York: Alfred A. Knopf, Inc., 1957.

## THE SOLAR SYSTEM

Aldiss, Brian W. (ed.). *All About Venus.* New York: Dell Publishing Co., Inc., 1968.*

Clarke, Arthur C. *The Promise of Space.* New York: Harper & Row, Publishers, 1968.

Dole, Stephen, and Isaac Asimov. *Planets for Man.* New York: Random House, Inc., 1964.

Gamow, George. *Birth and Death of the Sun.* New York: The Viking Press, Inc., 1949.*

Glasstone, Samuel. *Sourcebook on the Space Sciences.* Princeton: D. Van Nostrand Company, Inc., 1965.

Heide, Fritz. *Meteorites.* Chicago: University of Chicago Press, 1964.

Jackson, Joseph H. *Pictorial Guide to the Planets.* New York: Thomas Y. Crowell Company, 1965.

Jastrow, Robert, and A. G. W. Cameron (eds.). *Conference on the Origin of the Solar System.* New York: Academic Press, Inc., 1963.

Ohring, George. *Weather on the Planets: What We Know About Their Atmospheres.* Garden City, N.Y.: Doubleday & Company, Inc., 1965.*

Sagan, Carl, Jonathan N. Leonard, and the Editors of LIFE. *Planets.* New York: Time, Inc., 1966.

Watson, Fletcher G. *Between the Planets* (rev. ed.). Cambridge: Harvard University Press, 1959.*

Whipple, Fred L. *Earth, Moon and Planets* (3rd ed.). Cambridge: Harvard University Press, 1968.

# INDEX

*Italics indicate illustrations*

# A NOTE ON THIS BOOK

This book was published by the Editors of American Heritage Publishing Company in association with the Smithsonian Institution under the following editorial direction: For the Smithsonian Institution, Anders Richter, Director, Smithsonian Institution Press. For American Heritage, Editor, David G. McCullough; Managing Editor, Jean Atcheson; Art Director, Richard Glassman; Copy Editor, Susan Shapiro; Assistant Editors, Maria Ealand and Gay Sherry; Picture Editor, Martha F. Grossman; Editorial Assistants, Rita Levy and Susan J. Lewis.

## ACKNOWLEDGMENTS

The Editors wish to thank the following individuals and organizations for their valuable assistance:

Mrs. Cicely Breslin, Hayden Planetarium, Library, New York City

Dr. Owen Gingerich, Smithsonian Astrophysical Observatory, Cambridge, Mass.

Goddard Institute for Space Studies, Library, New York City

Barry Richman, Science Editor, American Heritage Dictionary, New York City

Dr. George Simon, Sacramento Peak Observatory, Sunspot, N. Mex.

Dr. Richard Stothers, Goddard Institute for Space Studies, New York City

## PICTURE CREDITS

Cover, Russ Kinne; Photo Researchers. 2, Mount Wilson and Palomar Observatories. 4–5, Ralph Crane; Black Star. 7, Cardamone Associates. 8–9, Dr. Georg Gerster; Rapho-Guillumette.
CHAPTER I: 10, The Bettmann Archive. 12–13 (both), Cardamone. 14–15 (top), Österreichische Nationalbibliothek, Vienna. 15, Royal Society, London. 16, Bibliothèque Publique et Universitaire, Geneva. 16–17, Erich Lessing; Magnum. 17, Giraudon. 18, Cardamone. 19, Johannes Kepler, *Commentaries on Mars.* 20, Cabinet des Dessins, Louvre. 21, Ufano, *Artillerie*, 1621; New York Public Library (NYPL). 22, New College, Oxford. 23, British Central Office of Information.
CHAPTER II: 24, Joe Munroe; Photo Researchers. 26, Smithsonian Institution. 27, Smithsonian Astrophysical Observatory. 28–29 (all), Dr. Georg Gerster; Rapho-Guillumette. 30 (top), Bell Telephone Laboratories. 30 (bottom), Imperial War Museum. 32, Mount Wilson and Palomar Observatories. 33, © Copyright 1959 by California Institute of Technology and Carnegie Institution of Washington. 34, Harvard College Observatory. 36 (top left and right), Ivan Massar; Black Star. 36 (bottom), Smithsonian.
CHAPTER III: 38, Ansel Adams. 40–41, Mount Wilson and Palomar Observatories. 42, Robert Hooke, *Micrographia*, 1665. 43, Jet Propulsion Laboratory (J.P.L.). 45, NASA. 46 (all), NYPL. 48–49, Paintings by Chesley Bonestell; courtesy International Space Museum and Gallery, Inc. 50–51, From "The Surface of the Moon," by Albert R. Hibbs. Copyright © 1967 by Scientific American, Inc. All rights reserved.
CHAPTER IV: 52, Emil Schulthess; Black Star. 54, Courtesy of the Metropolitan Museum of Art, Rogers Fund and contribution from Henry Walters, Purchase, 1916. 55, Richard Glassman. 56–57, Sacramento Peak Observatory, Air Force Cambridge Research Laboratories. 59 (top), Cardamone. 59 (bottom), UPI. 60 (all), Photoworld. 60–61 (top), *Harper's Weekly*, August 28, 1869. 61, 62–63, Emil Schulthess; Black Star. 64–67 (all), Kitt Peak National Observatory.
CHAPTER V: 68, J.P.L. 70 (top and bottom right), NASA. 70 (bottom left), J.P.L. 71, Sovfoto. 72, From *Sourcebook on the Space Sciences* by Samuel Glasstone, copyright 1965, D. Van Nostrand Company; redrawn by Cardamone. 73, Cardamone. 74, William S. Dalton. 76, Larry Lee. 77 (left), J.P.L. 77 (right), Cornell University.
CHAPTER VI: 78, © Copyright 1965 by California Institute of Technology and Carnegie Institution. 81 (top and bottom), Lowell Observatory. 81 (center), From *The Exploration of Mars* by Willy Ley and Wernher von Braun, Sidgwick and Jackson Ltd., London, 1956. 82–83, Lowell Observatory. 83, Yerkes Observatory. 84, H. G. Wells. 85 (left), *The New York Times* Studio. 85 (right), Culver Pictures. 86 (top), NASA. 86 (bottom), J.P.L. 86–87, Painting by Chesley Bonestell; courtesy International Space Museum and Gallery, Inc. 88, J.P.L., redrawn by Cardamone. 91, Yerkes Observatory.
CHAPTER VII: 92 (all), Yerkes Observatory. 95, New Mexico State Observatory. 98–99, © Copyright 1965 by California Institute of Technology and Carnegie Institution. 100 (left), Culver. 100 (right), Oldbourne Book Co. Ltd. 101, Culver. 102, Painting by Chesley Bonestell; courtesy International Space Museum and Gallery, Inc. 103, © Copyright 1965 by California Institute of Technology and Carnegie Institution. 104, Culver. 105, Yerkes Observatory. 106, The American Museum of Natural History. 107, UPI.
CHAPTER VIII: 108, The New-York Historical Society. 110, Mount Wilson and Palomar Observatories. 111, © Copyright 1965 by California Institute of Technology and Carnegie Institution. 113, NYPL. 114, 114–115, The American Museum of Natural History. 115, Spence Air Photos. 119, Ivan Massar; Black Star. 120–121 (all), Mount Wilson and Palomar Observatories. 121, The Bettmann Archive. 124, The diagram is from *The Double Helix* by James D. Watson, Atheneum Publishers, New York. Copyright © 1968 by James D. Watson. 125, National Portrait Gallery, London. 126, © Copyright 1959 by California Institute of Technology and Carnegie Institution. 128, Louis Nitka, © 1967 by Harper's Magazine, Inc.
APPENDIX: 133, NYPL. 134–135 (top), NYPL. 134–135 (all bottom), Cardamone. 136 (left), Alinari. 136 (right), Culver. 137, NYPL. 138, Culver. 139, Royal Society, London. 140 (top left and right), The Bettmann Archive. 140 (bottom), reprinted with permission of the publisher from *And There Was Light* by Rudolph Thiel. Copyright © 1957 by Alfred A. Knopf, Inc. 141, NYPL. 142–143, NYPL. 144 (top), Yerkes Observatory. 144 (bottom), Cardamone. 145, Ralph Crane; Black Star. 146–147, Clyde W. Tombaugh. 149, *The New York Times*. 151–153 (all), Culver. 154 (all), Metro-Goldwyn-Mayer, Inc.